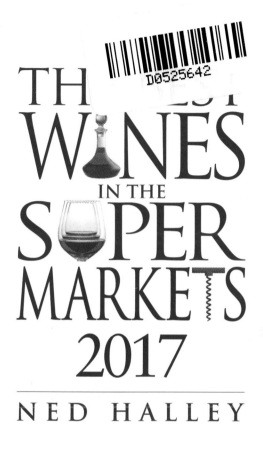

TH...
W🍷NES
IN THE
S🍷PER
MARKETS
2017

NED HALLEY

foulsham
LONDON • NEW YORK • TORONTO • SYDNEY

D0525642

W. Foulsham & Co. Ltd
for Foulsham Publishing Ltd
The Old Barrel Store, Drayman's Lane, Marlow, Bucks SL7 2FF

Foulsham books can be found in all good bookshops and direct from www.foulsham.com

ISBN: 978-0-572-04627-9

Printed and bound in Great Britain by Martins the Printers Ltd

Contents

There will always be wine

Now that we're on our way out of the European Union, what about wine? In the continuing aftermath of the shock vote for Brexit, the media has given this momentous matter scant attention. I did enjoy an article looking forward with eager excitement to the return of proper duty-free shops at ports and airports on European routes, but it will be many years before this nostalgic notion can be realized, if ever.

In the meantime I've been making polite enquiries amongst members of the wine trade. Will our erstwhile Continental neighbours refuse to sell us any more wine now that we've turned our backs on them? I always get the same answer. The winemakers will crawl over the proverbial broken glass (remember that one?) to continue supplying the UK. We are the principal export market for most of the European wine-producing countries. But the politicians and officials of those nations may see it differently.

Given our longer-term trading history with, say, France, vengeful behaviour at government level can't be ruled out. But it's far too early to anticipate sanctions. According to all sorts of experts, under Article 50 of the Lisbon Treaty, it could well be 2026 before departure is effected. Before then, tariff wars – EU whacks tax on spirits imported from UK and UK ripostes with taxes on EU wine imports – are very unlikely.

Other consequences of Brexit are easier to identify. If the pound's slump from its 2015 high of around 1.40 euros back to the previously prevailing 1.20 is maintained, the price of wines from the eurozone will naturally go up. Predicting the fortunes of sterling is, of course, a perilous business. Given the delicate economic state of so many EU member countries, would anybody wish to make a bet as I write now in summer 2016 on what the sterling exchange rate will be in, say, the summer of 2017?

The supermarkets will be trying hard to be predictive. When you spend billions on imported goods, every fractional shift in exchange rates has a palpable impact on profits. Poor dears. How do they manage? In fairness, Brexit must have been an unwelcome additional difficulty amidst all the other troubles of the big chains. They're all losing market share to the discounters (both European incomers, of course), mourning the demise of the Big Weekly Shop, waging price wars and trying to restructure themselves with an eye on the bottom line.

In this unending era of austerity 'everyday low prices' has become the mantra in supermarket retailing. It's hardly a new tune, of course, but it might just be the funeral anthem for that old friend of the wine customer and the principal promotional tool of supermarket wine retailing, the multibuy offer. The acknowledged motive for extinguishing this marketing mechanic is that encouraging us to buy more than we really want or need leads to waste and excess.

This might well be true for perishable foods. But wine? The ideal way to buy wine from a supermarket must surely be to do so in quantity. You pounce when your wine of choice is at its cheapest and squirrel it away. If you're sensible, you neither buy nor consume any more of it than you would on the basis of single-bottle purchases. You just make fewer journeys. Which is supposed to be a good thing in itself.

The idea of outlawing this commonsense consumer strategy via a ban on multibuys is a legacy of the Scottish Government. This fine body of legislators outlawed the promotion of alcohol sales by this method in 2011, but Parliament in Westminster has not followed suit. Alcohol consumption in Scotland is much higher than in England and Wales – about 17 per cent – and while recorded sales of alcohol are progressively down in volume terms, with the occasional, um, hiccup, the rate of decline is very much slower north of the border than it is to the south.

Pricing alcohol out of the reach of those to whom it is deemed to do most harm has always been a cornerstone of prohibitionist consumer legislation. But in the Scottish experiment it has so far looked ineffective. And if supermarkets nationwide are not made to end the promotional discounting of drinks products, I can't see them doing it voluntarily. For all the trumpeting of everyday low prices, most of the big chains continue to offer periodical blanket discounts, usually of 25 per cent, on all their wines. Sainsbury's and Tesco, who mysteriously seem consistently to coincide in the matter, apply these promos even to wines on individual discount. That makes for some spectacular bargains. Long may it continue.

Ups and downs at the Dept of Health

If you inspect the back labels of many supermarket wines you'll find guidelines on healthy drinking which advise that men should not exceed 3 to 4 units a day and women 2 to 3 units a day. This advice is now out of date. The UK Department of Health lowered its recommended safe maximum alcohol allowance to 2 units per day for men and women alike in February 2016, but it did not trouble to warn the drinks trade in advance. Countless millions of labels had already been printed with the redundant data.

At the time of the announcement, the media widely reported that the limits before the 2016 revision were 21 and 14 units respectively. Not true. As the current, outdated label information intimates, the recommended limits were 28 units for men and 21 for women. These had prevailed since 1995. They had previously been 21 and 14, but only since 1987. Prior to that, the recommended number of units had been 56.

A bottle of wine at 13% alcohol contains about 10 units.

Wine is probably more affordable in real terms in Britain right now than it has ever been. Even the scandalous excise duty imposed on every 75cl of still wine, up to £2.08 from £2.05 in the 2016 Budget, has not exterminated the sub-£5 bottle – I have picked out dozens of genuinely delicious examples in this edition – and the profusion in the mid-price zone of £6 to £10 is a marvel.

Variety and quality have not been sacrificed by the supermarkets on the altar of value. Even Aldi and Lidl, to whom I find myself dedicating more and more space in each successive edition of this book, are moving consciously upmarket with their gleefully hyped offers from Bordeaux and Burgundy, classic regions of Italy and Spain, and of course Champagne.

It's an extremely competitive market, supplied by a worldwide industry whose output increases continually. The retailers have the whip hand, and it is widely assumed that the biggest ones – that'll be the supermarkets – treat their suppliers badly. This is probably true in some cases, but over the years I have heard fewer complaints from the producers and their agents than I might have expected.

And there is a common purpose in supermarket wine retailing these days that calls upon both sides to co-operate constructively. It's the business of producing own-label wines and exclusive brands. All the supermarkets now participate in making the wines to which they put their own names. And as own-label ranges such as Morrisons Signature and Sainsbury's Taste the Difference grow in number and significance on shelf, so does the dependence of the supermarket on the reliability of the producer. Mutuality makes better wine.

It's the own-label wines that dominate in this book. They're the wines that matter most to the supermarkets and the wines that define them, too. They are the wines most frequently discounted, which invariably adds to their attractiveness.

The scores I allocate to all the wines are based on value judgment. I take into account the quoted shelf price. With all the discounting that goes on, my scoring system can inevitably become distorted, but look at it this way: if you find a 9-scoring wine at £7 instead of the £10 I've quoted, you're going to think well of it.

Please take my scores in the spirit I intend them. They are subjective in qualitative terms and entirely connected to my notions of value for money. Nearly all the wines are allocated scores of 8 upwards simply because there isn't space for wines I have liked less. The occasional low score goes to wines I have really liked, but believed overpriced. A nice discount would take care of that, of course, but I cannot presume. Some wines are good prospects but I believe need time to come round. And a very few wines are low-scored because I've paid for them and they've been a bitter disappointment. Childish vengefulness.

Wines scoring 8 are always good and good value. At 9, there is special merit and special value too. The maximum scores are wines I hope everyone will try because they are bang-on for character, quality and value.

In my little descriptions, I include the alcohol levels quoted for every wine that is below 12 per cent by volume or above 13 per cent. I hope this is of help to wine drinkers who are interested.

Almost all the wines here are made from the grape harvest of the year stated on the label. If no date appears, the wine has been blended from more than a single year's crop. This is routine for some generic wines and need not signify except in the case of dry whites. Best advice is buy these with a date on them, and the more recent the date, the better.

Finally, please understand that all my descriptions and evaluations are based on my own very singular judgment. Taste, as everybody knows, is very personal in everything. And wine is by no means an exception.

A sense of place

This book categorises the wines by nation of origin. It is largely to follow the manner in which retailers arrange their wines, but also because it is the country or region of origin that still most distinguishes one style of wine from another. True, wines are now commonly labelled most prominently with their constituent grape variety, but to classify all the world's wines into the small number of principal grape varieties would make for categories of an unwieldy size.

Chardonnay, Sauvignon Blanc and Pinot Grigio are overwhelmingly dominant among whites, and four grapes – Cabernet Sauvignon, Grenache, Merlot and Syrah (also called Shiraz) – account for a high proportion of red wines made worldwide.

But each area of production still – in spite of creeping globalisation – puts its own mark on its wines. Chardonnays from France remain (for the moment at least) quite distinct from those of Australia. Cabernet Sauvignon grown in a cool climate such as that of Bordeaux is a very different wine from Cabernet cultivated in the cauldron of the Barossa.

Of course there are 'styles' that winemakers worldwide seek to follow. Yellow, oaky Chardonnays of the type pioneered in South Australia are now made in South Africa, too – and in new, high-tech wineries in New Zealand and Chile, Spain and Italy. But the variety is still wide. Even though the 'upfront' high-alcohol wines of the New World have grabbed so much of the market, France continues to make the elegant wines it has always made in its classic regions. Germany still produces racy, delicate Rieslings, and the distinctive zones of Italy, Portugal and Spain make ever more characterful wines from indigenous grapes, as opposed to imported global varieties.

Among less expensive wines, the theme is, admittedly, very much a varietal one. The main selling point for most 'everyday' wines is the grape of origin rather than the country of origin. It makes sense, because the characteristics of various grape varieties do a great deal to identify taste. A bottle of white wine labelled 'Chardonnay' can reasonably be counted on to deliver that distinctive peachy or pineappley smell and soft, unctuous apple flavours. A Sauvignon Blanc should evoke gooseberries, green fruit and grassy freshness. And so on.

For all the domination of Chardonnay and Cabernet, there are plenty of other grape varieties making their presence felt. Argentina, for example, has revived the fortunes of several French and Italian varieties that had become near-extinct at home. And the grape that (in my view) can make the most exciting of white wines, the Riesling, is now doing great things in the southern hemisphere as well as at home in Germany.

Among the current market trends, the rise of rosé continues apace. Now accounting for one out of every eight bottles of still wine sold, the choice of pink brands has simply exploded. I have certainly found a greater number of interesting pinks than might have been imagined a few years ago, but there are still plenty of dull ones with suspiciously high levels of residual sugar, so choose carefully.

Rosé wines are supposed to be made from black-skinned grapes. After the crush, the skins are left in contact with the juice for long enough to impart a pleasing colour, and maybe some flavour with it, and the liquids and solids are then separated before the winemaking process continues as it would for white wine.

Some rosés are made merely by blending red and white wines together. Oddly enough, this is how all (bar one or two) pink champagnes are made, as permitted under the local appellation rules. But under prevailing regulations in Europe, the practice is otherwise forbidden. Elsewhere in the world, where winemaking is very much less strictly standardised, blending is no doubt common enough.

It is, I know, a perpetual source of anguish to winemakers in tightly regulated European nations that they have to compete in important markets like Britain with producers in Australia, the Americas and South Africa who can make and label their wines just as they please. Vineyard irrigation, the use of oak chips, and the blending in of wines from other continents are all permitted in the New World and eschewed in the Old.

But would we have it any other way? No winemaker I have met in Bordeaux or Barolo, Bernkastel or Rias Baixas seriously wants to abandon the methods and conventions that make their products unique – even with an eye on creating a global brand. And in this present difficult economic climate for wine drinkers (and winemakers) worldwide, this assurance of enduring diversity is a comfort indeed.

Spot the grape
variety

The character of most wines is defined largely by the grape variety, and it is a source of innocent pleasure to be able to identify which variety it is without peeking at the label. Here are some of the characteristics to look for in wines from the most widely planted varieties.

White

Chardonnay: Colour from pale to straw gold. Aroma can evoke peach, pineapple, sweet apple. Flavours of sweet apple, with creaminess or toffee from oak contact.

Fiano: Italian variety said to have been cultivated from ancient Roman times in the Campania region of southern Italy. Now widely planted on the mainland and in Sicily, it makes dry but soft wines of colours ranging from pale to pure gold with aromas of honey, orchard fruit, almonds and candied apricot. Well-made examples have beautifully balanced nutty-fresh flavours. Fiano is becoming fashionable.

Pinot Grigio: In its home territory of north-east Italy, it makes wines of pale colour, and pale flavour too. What makes the wine so popular might well be its natural low acidity. Better wines are more aromatic, even smoky, and pleasingly weighty in the manner of the Pinot Gris made in Alsace – now being convincingly imitated in both Argentina and New Zealand.

Riesling: In German wines, pale colour, sharp-apple aroma, racy fruit whether dry or sweet. Faint spritz common in young wines. Petrolly hint in older wines. Australian and New Zealand Rieslings have more colour and weight, and often a minerally, limey twang.

Sauvignon Blanc: In the dry wines, pale colour with suggestions of green. Aromas of asparagus, gooseberries, nettles, seagrass. Green, grassy fruit.

Semillon: Colour can be rich yellow. Aromas of tropical fruit including pineapple and banana. Even in dry wines, hints of honey amid fresh, fruit-salad flavours.

Viognier: Intense pale-gold colour. Aroma evokes apricots, blanched almonds and fruit blossom. Flavours include candied fruits. Finish often low in acidity.

Red

Cabernet Sauvignon: Dense colour, purple in youth. Strong aroma of blackcurrants and cedar wood ('cigar box'). Flavour concentrated, often edged with tannin so it grips the mouth.

Gamay: One of the most distinctive grapes of France, where it is the exclusive variety in the red wines of Beaujolais. Colour can be purple, with a suggestion of blue; nose evokes new-squashed raspberries, and there may be a hint of pear drops, an effect of carbonic maceration, a vinification technique used in Beaujolais. Fruit flavours are notably summery, juicy and refreshing.

Grenache: Best known in the Côtes du Rhône, it tends to make red wines pale in colour but forceful in flavour with a wild, hedgerow-fruit style and hints of pepper.

Malbec: Originally a Bordeaux variety, Malbec has become principally renowned in Argentina, where it thrives in the high-altitude vineyards of Mendoza. Wines are characterised by very dark, dense colour, and by aromas that perhaps fancifully evoke leather and liquorice as well as dark fruits. Flavours include black fruits with chocolate and spice; the wines are often grippy with retained tannin.

Merlot: Dark, rich colour. Aroma of sweet black cherry. Plummy, rich, mellow fruit can be akin to Cabernet but with less tannin. May be hints of bitter chocolate.

Pinot Noir: Colour distinctly pale, browning with age. Aromas of strawberry and raspberry. Light-bodied wine with soft-fruit flavours but dry, clean finish.

Sangiovese: The grape of Chianti and now of several other Italian regions, too. Colour is fine ruby, and may be relatively light; a plummy or even pruny smell is typical, and flavours can evoke blackcurrant, raspberry and nectarine. Tannin lingers, so the wine will have a dry, nutskin-like finish.

Shiraz or Syrah: Intense, near-black colour. Aroma of ripe fruit, sometimes spicy. Robust, rich flavours, commonly with high alcohol, but with soft tannins. The Shiraz of Australia is typically much more substantial than the Syrah of the south of France.

Tempranillo: Colour can be pale, as in Rioja. Blackcurrant aroma, often accompanied by vanilla from oak ageing. Tobacco, even leather, evoked in flavours.

There is more about all these varieties, and many others, in 'What wine words mean' starting on page 155.

Looking for a branded wine?

While the supermarkets' own-label wines – the likes of the Sainsbury's Taste the Difference and the Tesco Finest ranges – are obviously exclusive to the respective chains, branded wines are very often stocked by any number of different retailers.

If you're looking for a favourite brand, do check the index to this book on page 189. If I have tasted the wine and given it a mention, it is most likely to appear under the heading of the supermarket that hosted the tasting. But you might be accustomed to seeing this particular wine in another chain altogether.

I cannot give space in a pocket-sized book to repetitions of notes on popular brands that might very well be sold by each of the supermarket chains. But I do try to keep tasting the bestselling brands in hope of finding something positive to say about them.

First impressions
—————*count*—————

I have an uncomfortable feeling that singling out just 24 wines from the many hundreds tasted in the course of preparing this book is an invidious action. It is, in the dictionary definition, offensively discriminating. It's likely to cause envy, or for that matter sincere disagreement.

But I can't resist. I allocate these maximum scores at the moment of tasting because I believe in first impressions. When I start to count them up at the end of the months of tasting, I have no idea how many there will be or, more interestingly, whether there will be any pattern.

So here's the breakdown. Of the 24 wines that I've scored 10, 14 are red wines, eight are whites and two are sparklers. Countries of origin come out as follows: France 7; Spain 5; Italy 4; Germany and New Zealand both 2; 1 apiece for Argentina, Australia, Chile and Uruguay. Any detectable pattern? I'm still trying to work it out.

What most definitely would be invidious would be to claim that the retailer with the most top scores is better than the others. I'm not going to express any preferences, especially in this time of extraordinary upheaval for all the supermarkets.

But here's how my top-scoring wines are distributed: Asda, M&S and Sainsbury's 4; Waitrose 3; Aldi, the Co-op and Majestic 2 apiece; Lidl, Morrisons and Tesco 1 apiece.

Red wines

Extra Special Barbera d'Asti 2013	Asda	£5.00
La Moneda Reserva Merlot 2015	Asda	£5.75
Exquisite Collection Cabernet de Cabernet 2014	Aldi	£5.99
Domaine du Colombier Chinon 2013	Sainsbury's	£7.00
Finest Ribera del Duero 2011	Tesco	£7.00
Noster Nobilis Priorat 2013	Asda	£7.98
Paz Cabernet Sauvignon Cabernet Franc 2014	Co-op	£8.49
Pisano Cisplatino Tannat 2015	M&S	£9.00
The Cubist Old Vine Calatayud Garnacha 2014	Waitrose	£9.99
Taste the Difference Château Tanunda Barossa Cabernet Merlot 2014	Sainsbury's	£10.00
Taste the Difference Cepa Alegro Rioja Reserva 2010	Sainsbury's	£10.00
Palataia Pinot Noir 2014	M&S	£10.50
Definition Rioja Reserva 2009	Majestic	£11.99
Extra Special Barolo 2011	Asda	£12.00

White wines

Bianco Vino da Tavola 2015	M&S	£5.00
Freeman's Bay Marlborough Sauvignon Blanc 2015	Aldi	£5.89
Côtes de Gascogne Le Heron 2015	Lidl	£5.99
The Ned Pinot Grigio 2015	Waitrose	£9.45
Reichsgraf von Kesselstatt Goldtröpfchen Riesling Kabinett 2014	Co-op	£9.99
Vouvray Domaine des Aubuisières Cuvée de Perruches 2014	Majestic	£9.99
Ascheri Langhe Arneis 2014	M&S	£13.00
Signature Chablis 1er Cru 2013	Morrisons	£15.00

Sparkling wines

Winemakers' Selection Blanc de Noir Champagne Brut	Sainsbury's	£20.00
Waitrose Brut Special Réserve Vintage 2005	Waitrose	£24.99

Aldi

'The principal attraction of Aldi's wines,' I wrote here in the 2007 edition of this guide, 'is, I suppose, the price'.

A decade is clearly a long time in discount retailing. Aldi's UK network consisted of 250 stores in 2007 and by 2017 will have exceeded 700. Annual sales have already surpassed those of Waitrose and may soon eclipse those of the Co-op.

Today, Aldi claims to sell one in every 13 bottles of wine bought in the UK. And price doesn't really come into it. Of the fifty wines I have picked out from the range this year, only a dozen cost under a fiver.

Quality and diversity now rank higher than mere 'everyday lower prices' (to quote the current supermarket-retailing mantra) at Aldi. The choice is improving fast, all the wines are own-label or exclusive, and in addition to the established 'Exquisite Collection' brand there is a new premium range called the Lot Series from around the world, all smartly packaged and priced at £9.99. Some of them are very good, and good value too.

Another new development is Aldi's online home-delivery operation. It was launched early in 2016 and will ultimately be extended to all sorts of products, but the service began with wine only. Fortunately, I was invited to taste the Aldi range this year – after missing out in 2015 – so I have not had to resort to buying the wines. While I was very grateful to Aldi for kindly including me among the numbers at their excellent tasting, I was just a little disappointed to discover that many of the wines that I had liked best are on sale only via the website.

I do think it's a pity that the whole range cannot be offered to customers in the stores. Maybe as the branch network continues to expand at its present breakneck rate, space will be found.

RED WINES

AUSTRALIA

🍷 8 **Exquisite Collection Limestone
Coast Cabernet 2014** £6.49
A rather restrained – dare I say Bordeaux-like – Cabernet
Sauvignon; balanced blackcurranty-ripe food wine at a
sensible price; 14% alcohol.

🍷 8 **A.C. Byrne McLaren Vale Shiraz 2014** £7.49
Generous ripe roasty-spicy black-fruit monster has poise
and briskness; 14.5% alcohol. Online only.

🍷 8 **The Lot Series Clare-Coonawarra
Cabernet Sauvignon 2014** £9.99
The 300-mile distance between the vineyard regions
of Clare and Coonawarra is not detectable in this
harmonious, lushly dark and cassis-rich package,
finishing very trim; 14% alcohol. Online only.

🍷 9 **Estevez Pinot Noir 2013** £4.89
Alluring limpid ruby-bronze colour, strawberry nose and
fleshy sweet but trim red-fruit juiciness in this charming
midweight Pinot; bargain.

🍷 8 **Estevez Cabernet-Carmenère 2014** £4.89
Enticing toffee note on the nose of this artful blend;
convincing berry fruit and clean finish; 13.5% alcohol.

CHILE

🍷 9 **The Lot Series Colchagua Carmenère 2012** £9.99
In Aldi's smartly presented premium range, a properly
distinctive mature varietal with inky purple colour in
spite of age, and lashings of ripe briary-mulberry creamy
black fruit, neatly tannin-trimmed; 14% alcohol. Online
only.

RED WINES

FRANCE

🍷 **9** **Vignobles Rousselet Pinot Noir**   £4.39
This Beaujolais-like non-vintage blend of Pinot Noir from the Loire and Merlot from Languedoc is vivid, juicy and wholesome with cherry-raspberry brightness; amiable summery red to try cool.

🍷 **8** **Vignobles Rousselet Malbec**   £4.39
Darkly purple non-vintage Languedoc coaly-spicy winter red; includes 15% Syrah for added sleekness and is impressively cheap.

🍷 **9** **Venturer Series Costières de Nîmes 2013**   £4.79
Dense, dark and spicy Med red is grippingly convincing at this low price; 14% alcohol. Online only.

🍷 **8** **Exquisite Collection Fitou 2014**   £5.49
Comfortably grippy black-fruit winter red from near-extinct Languedoc appellation has spice and durability.

🍷 **7** **Exquisite Collection Fleurie 2014**   £5.49
Fleurie is one of the high-fallutin' 'crus' of Beaujolais, but this more resembles an everyday Beaujolais-Villages in character as well as price; nice fruity glugger.

🍷 **10** **Exquisite Collection Cabernet de Cabernet 2014**   £5.99
A 50/50 Cabernet Franc and Cabernet Sauvignon Languedoc mix, this ideally balances the arch green crunchiness of the one with the cassis richness of the other in a substantial, satisfying and superior concoction; masterly winemaking and 13.5% alcohol.

RED WINES

9 **Château Larteau 2010** £8.99
Whoppingly ripe (14.5% alcohol) pure Merlot Bordeaux
Supérieur from a renowned vintage; silky with sweet
blackcurrant notes, still coming round but already
warmly mellow; drink or keep – a bargain. Online only.

9 **The Lot Series Metairie de**
   Bois Corbières 2013 £9.99
Aldi's own 'The Lot' premium wine range is attractively
packaged in antique-style heavy glass with tie-on tags in
addition to elegant labels. This is one of several that live
up well to the hype: smoothly oaked Med red with plenty
of black-fruit oomph, spice and roasty richness; 14.5%
alcohol.

8 **Jean Bouchard Hautes Côtes de Nuits 2013** £9.99
Authentic pale Burgundy with good raspberry intensity,
crunchy liveliness and a lemon twang at the finish. Online
only.

8 **The Lot Series Minervois La Livinière 2014** £9.99
This darkly spicy-truffly Syrah-dominated winter wine
will develop for 6 to 8 years according to the label; good
muscular red-meat matcher now, with 14% alcohol.

9 **Château Solcil Puisseguin-St-Emilion 2009** £11.99
Gently ageing St Emilion satellite shows chocolate in
the colour and matching spicy richness in the fruit; it's a
cracking claret from a fabled vintage at a sensible price,
14.5% alcohol. Online only.

8 **Jean Bouchard Beaune 2013** £16.99
Proper pricy red Burgundy, has a lick of creamy oak on
the nose and in the delicate but plump Pinot fruit; classy
if not exactly a bargain. Online only.

RED WINES

🍷 8 **Castellore Sicilian Shiraz 2014** £3.99
Well-knit sunny party red with hill-herb warmth.

🍷 9 **The Venturer Series Primitivo 2015** £4.99
Sweet plummy aroma and nutty-raisiny richness are nicely balanced by the defined red fruit and pleasingly raspy tannin in this interesting spaghetti red from Puglia. Grows on you.

🍷 8 **La Altalena Barolo 2011** £9.99
Naff-looking package but this is bona fide Barolo, pale and coppery in colour, spirity and spiky on the nose, silky rich and long in savoury fruit; 14% alcohol. Online only.

🍷 8 **The Lot Series Toscana Super Tuscan 2014** £9.99
'Super Tuscan' is an informal designation for posh reds made in Chianti country from non-indigenous grapes. This one is mostly from Bordeaux varieties Petit Verdot and Merlot plus a fraction of Sangiovese, the Chianti grape. Result: a thoroughly Italian red with dark brambly savour trimmed with nutskin tannic grip; excellent with pasta. Online only.

🍷 8 **La Sogara Amarone 2012** £11.49
These speciality Valpolicella wines are now ubiquitous, but usually very expensive. This one makes a reasonably priced introduction to the style, dark and gravid with coffee notes to the burnt intensity of the red fruit and a raspy finish; 15% alcohol. Online only.

RED WINES

NEW ZEALAND

🍷 8 **Exquisite Collection Hawke's Bay 'Bordeaux Blend' 2014** £6.99

This Bordeaux blend is two-thirds Merlot, making a nice black-cherry, minty and plump classic Kiwi 'claret' with 13.5% alcohol. Online only.

🍷 8 **Exquisite Collection New Zealand Pinot Noir 2014** £6.99

Kiwi Pinot is often pricy, so sample the style via this pale but interesting cheapie: straight cherry-fruit, brightly refreshing; 14% alcohol.

S. AFRICA

🍷 8 **Stellenbosch Cape Red** £5.99

Largely Shiraz and Cabernet Sauvignon, a non-vintage sweet blackberry blend with wholesome balance; 14.5% alcohol.

SPAIN

🍷 8 **Toro Loco Superior 2014** £3.49

Tempranillo-Bobal blend from Utiel-Requena is entirely plausible even at this inexplicable price; wholesome red-fruit savour in good balance.

🍷 8 **Toro Loco Bobal Merlot 2014** £4.69

'Aged in oak' it says in presumed justification of the price hike over Toro Loco Superior (above) and it does have a lick of vanilla amid the pleasant blackberry juiciness.

🍷 8 **Exquisite Collection Ribera del Duero 2014** £5.99

Dark cassis-eucalyptus-cinnamon allusions in this just-recognisable example of the exotic Ribera del Duero style at an unrecognisable price for the region. Online only.

RED WINES

SPAIN

🍷 8 **The Lot Series Priorat 2014** £9.99
Big liquorice-black-fruit nose reels you into the delights of
this handsomely packaged pure Garnacha from prestigious
Priorat region; darkly intense and savoury it tastes almost
as good as it looks; 14.5% alcohol. Online only.

WHITE WINES

AUSTRALIA

🍷 9 **Exquisite Collection Clare
Valley Riesling 2014** £6.99
Award-winner from last year still full of limey life, racy,
apple-crisp and lingering.

🍷 8 **Exquisite Collection Hunter
Valley Semillon 2013** £6.99
Dry aperitif wine with paradoxical exotic aromas and
flavours of peach and pineapple, banana and mango in
an attention-grabbing package; fun wine with just 11%
alcohol.

FRANCE

🍷 8 **Vignobles Rousselet Sauvignon Blanc** £4.39
A wee bit cheaper than last year's and a bit less lively but
a recognisable gooseberry style, easy on acidity.

🍷 8 **The Venturer Series Côtes de
Gascogne 2015** £4.79
Artful dry Atlantic refresher mixing green tang with a lick
of sunny ripeness; 11.5% alcohol.

🍷 9 **Exquisite Collection Marsanne 2015** £5.99
Alluring lemon-gold colour, peachy-sweet-pear perfume
and sunny ripeness marks this dry-finishing Mediterranean
refresher by talented Jean-Paul Mas. A treat on its own
but a match, too, for awkward salads; 13.5% alcohol.

WHITE WINES

FRANCE

🍷 8 **Exquisite Collection Clairette 2015**   £5.99
This beguiling tropical-fruit-salad-scented dry Languedoc wine has substance and freshness, made for outdoor drinking.

🍷 8 **Exquisite Collection Limoux**
    Chardonnay 2014   £6.99
A decided sherbet tingle to this Languedoc sweet-apple varietal gives it agreeable distinctiveness; 13.5% alcohol. Online only.

🍷 8 **André Vannier Chablis 2014**   £7.99
Correct mineral-stony style from this inimitable appellation showing long Chardonnay fruit; better value than the accompanying Vannier 1er Cru Chablis.

🍷 8 **The Lot Series Anjou Chenin Blanc 2012**   £9.99
Loire Valley lovely from the charismatic Chenin grape has daisy freshness and lush honeyed ripeness in sublime balance; well-presented premium wine.

ITALY

🍷 9 **Exquisite Collection Gavi 2015**   £5.49
Piedmont dry white, has a pungent nose reminiscent of fino sherry followed up by a stimulating pungency of crisp orchard fruit and a notion of almondy creaminess; fascinating, delicious bargain.

🍷 8 **La Altalena Gavi di Gavi 2014**   £6.99
Elegant, fresh and nuanced Gavi – good of its kind but less interesting than its cheaper stablemate above; 11.5% alcohol. Online only.

WHITE WINES

NEW ZEALAND

🍷 **10** Freeman's Bay Marlborough
Sauvignon Blanc 2015 £5.89
On the whole Aldi wines don't impress me as particularly cheap, but this one is – with no reflection on its quality. It glitters with proper Kiwi Sauvignon zest, full of green grass and asparagus flashes and satisfying in its length and intensity.

🍷 **8** The Lot Series Marlborough
Sauvignon Blanc 2015 £9.99
Complex oaked wine with masses of extracted grassy-nettly fruit for special occasions, smartly packaged; 13.5% alcohol.

S. AFRICA

🍷 **9** The Lot Series Bushvine Chenin
Blanc 2015 £9.99
Nice gold colour, orchard blossom and nectar on the nose and finely balanced lush-crisp complex peachy fruit in this impressive package to match tricky menus from fish to fowl, salads to Asian; 14% alcohol.

SPARKLING WINES

FRANCE

🍷 **9** Philippe Michel Crémant du Jura 2013 £7.29
Another year, another cracking vintage for this Aldi perennial from the high country east of Burgundy. The lifting apple-crisp Chardonnay freshness is carried along in the perky crémant foam induced by proper in-bottle fermentation; quality fizz at a consistently keen price.

🍷 **8** Exquisite Collection Blanquette de Limoux £7.99
Brut-style (briskly dry) fizz from Pyrenean foothills owing its distinctive orchard flavour to its constituent Mauzac grape, locally known as Blanquette. Eager party pop with a nice biscuity whiff.

SPARKLING WINES

FRANCE

8 **Veuve Monsigny Champagne Brut** £10.99
The standard shelf price of Aldi's house champagne
seems to fall annually by £1 but the quality persists. Tight
mousse, bakery aroma, crisp but rounded fruit.

8 **Veuve Monsigny Champagne Rosé Brut** £13.99
Pink champagne always costs more, and this one does at
least warrant it; fine salmon colour, tinge of strawberry
on the bready nose, rush of vivid flavour hinting at soft
summer red fruit.

ITALY

8 **Prosecco Valdobbiadene Superiore** £7.49
Baffled as I am by the Prosecco phenomenon – the tank-
made Venetian frother now outsells champagne – I can
just about see the joy in this pale, foaming, elderflower-
scented, dry example at 11% alcohol; no reason to pay
more than this.

Asda

Asda continues to impress with its wines, but will it last? Philippa Carr, the Master of Wine who did so much to create today's inspired range, has left the company. In 2016, shortly after accepting the *Decanter* magazine Wine Supermarket of the Year award on behalf of Asda, the American-owned giant expressed its appreciation by bringing Philippa's ten-years of service to an end in some sort of management restructure.

It is a decision the executives at Asda might, I fear, come to regret, but I nevertheless wish the new wine manager well. He has a lot to live up to, as I believe Asda closely rivals Sainsbury's for the quality and diversity of its wines, easily outclasses Tesco and for value is ahead of all the competition – Aldi and Lidl included.

Of the 50 Asda wines I've described this year, more than half are priced at £6 or below – extending right down to a Spanish red at £3.29, the cheapest drinkable wine I have tried in a long time, and really quite good. There are some cracking Italian reds at various price levels, and several serious Loire Valley whites at the fine-wine end of the scale.

Asda is not unique in the variation of choice offered in its stores. I have two branches near to home, one a giant that has just about every wine I can think of, the other a flung-up pre-fab affair that seems never to have anything I'm after. Naturally, the well-stocked store is twice as far away.

So to play safe, I've taken to ordering wine from Asda's 'Wine Shop' online. The website looks old-fashioned to me, and this enables me to understand it that much better. Very many of the wines – though by no means all – are listed, and discounts, of which there are always many, are clearly displayed. There are even a few wines exclusive to the online service. Delivery is free if you order a sensible quantity and my last order reached me the day after I ordered it.

I sincerely hope that in this space next year I will be able to report with equal enthusiasm on Asda's wine offering.

RED WINES

ARGENTINA

8 **Trapiche Malbec 2013** £9.98

Benchmark Mendoza roast-beef red is elegantly poised and lush – not overcooked as some Malbecs can be – and wholesomely ripe; 14.5% alcohol.

AUSTRALIA

8 **Extra Special Barossa Shiraz 2015** £5.98

Safe, good-value, wholesomely ripe and gripping winter red with fleeting spice and creaminess and 14% alcohol.

8 **Extra Special Yarra Valley Pinot Noir 2015** £7.98

Pale, cool, cherry-raspberry wine by excellent De Bortoli in Victoria is made in what I call the old Burgundy style – that is, with the addition of a bit of Shiraz.

CHILE

9 **Wine Atlas Carmenère 2014** £4.97

Dark maroon colour is, I guess, the 'carmine' embodied in the grape's name, and the distinctiveness of the wine ('the signature wine of Chile' asserts the label) continues into sweetly ripe forest-fruit aroma, savoury-sweet black fruit and taut finish; lovely stuff at a very keen price; 13.6% alcohol.

10 **La Moneda Reserva Merlot 2015** £5.75

Bright crimson colour, lashings of black-cherry plumpness and artfully contrived balance; don't let the naff metallised label put you off one of the best supermarket wine bargains of the year.

9 **Marea Syrah 2012** £11.97

Blood-red, opulent, velvety pure varietal is a kind of Chilean (Leyda Valley) Côte Rôtie showing ritzy spice and mulberry through the rich but well-judged oak; a very warming and reassuring reminder that Chile can really do it; 14.5% alcohol.

RED WINES

Asda

FRANCE

🍷 8 **Extra Special Shiraz 2014** £6.00

It makes me grind my teeth when they label the Syrah of France with the Australian synonym Shiraz, but this is a fine, crunchy-spicy Languedoc – not Languedoz – with vigorous but slinky blackberry fruit; 13.5% alcohol.

🍷 9 **Extra Special Bordeaux Rouge**
Château Roberperots 2012 £7.00

This same wine featured in last year's edition for its 'promising dense colour, cedary-cassis nose and sleek, unified, distinctly claret-like fruit'. Now, it's mellowed with bottle age, though still firm with tannin, and the price has dropped from £10 to £7. Bargain.

🍷 8 **Le Grand Clauzy Pinot Noir 2014** £7.45

Imitation red Burgundy from the sun-baked Hérault has attractive pale colour, sweet cherry nose in which a sprinkle of chocolate lurks and bright, earthy convincing Pinot savour.

🍷 8 **Hauts de Janeil Syrah Grenache 2014** £9.00

Hearty, dense, spicy black-fruit Languedoc gripper will make a satisfying partner to meaty-starchy dishes such as cassoulet. Wine shop online.

ITALY

🍷 9 **Wine Atlas Frappato 2014** £4.97

Lively red-berry-fruit varietal from Sicily, still vigorously drinkable in its second year (I reported enthusiastically on this same vintage in the last edition) and very attractively labelled; good match for saucy fish dishes and pasta – and at a bargain price.

RED WINES

10 Extra Special Barbera d'Asti 2013 £5.00
Made by Piedmont giant Araldica, which seems to supply just about every supermarket, this nevertheless stood out for me this year. You get a spiffingly lurid deep crimson colour, sweet-briar aroma and matching bouncy-juicy fruit made extra lush by way of partial oak-ageing; a delightful artifice of substance (14.5% alcohol) and perkiness; seems madly underpriced.

8 Extra Special Montepulciano
d'Abruzzo 2014 £5.00
Rustic sweet-briar style, as expected, to this popular Adriatic varietal at a popular price.

8 Extra Special Primitivo 2013 £5.00
Dark, oak-sleeked Puglian has a liquorice-like ripeness and coaly grip of tannin but a friendly demeanour within; you get a lot of savour for the money; 13.5% alcohol.

9 Orbitali Squinzano Riserva 2011 £5.98
Left over from last year, when it was online only at £8.98, this oaked black-fruit smoothie from the tatty little Salerno town of Squinzano (delirious name!) has a twinge of spice and good abrasion at the finish; bargain.

8 Extra Special Chianti Riserva 2013 £6.00
Vivid fruit is standing up to the two years' ageing in oak so that it tastes positively perky, like proper everyday Chianti should; good price.

ITALY

RED WINES

8 **Villa Vincini Il Gran Rosso 2015** £7.48

An odd mix of Merlot with Corvina (as in Valpolicella) this stygian purple-ruby monster has rampant black fruit with flashes of sweetness and lots of plump heft; I loved it and imagine it the ideal roast-beef red: the horseradish won't stand a chance; 14% alcohol.

10 **Extra Special Barolo 2011** £12.00

Ordinary-looking package reveals an outstanding Barolo bargain – a rarity indeed. Alluring limpid bricky colour draws you to the seductive, sumptuous bunch-of-roses nose and flavours of slinkiest red fruits, ineffably complex and enticing, luxuriantly ripe (14.5% alcohol) but perfectly poised. The bargain price (for Barolo) is the cherry on the cake.

9 **Orbitali Brunello di Montalcino 2010** £14.98

This super-Chianti is in Italy's top rank of prestige names, but in my bitter experience, often disappoints. Here's one to try: it's in dignified middle age showing a nice brown tinge in the colour, a near-spirity high-toned grand-Chianti-like nose and delivering long, silky, black Tuscan fruits with notions of coffee, black-cherry and correct roasty pungency, all in elegant harmony with 14.5% alcohol. It tastes suitably expensive.

8 **Extra Special New Zealand Pinot Noir 2013** £7.98

Pale but interesting Marlborough wine in the hallmark cherry-minty Kiwi style at a fair price; 13.5% alcohol.

ITALY

N. ZEALAND

RED WINES

S. AFRICA

♟ 8 **Extra Special Fairtrade Shiraz 2015** £5.00
Defined dark sun-baked and spicy everyday red from the
Western Cape, very cheap for what it is; 14.5% alcohol.

SPAIN

♟ 8 **Carlos Minairo Tempranillo 2014** £3.29
Look at the price! It doesn't compute, but the wine, a
legitimate light La Mancha party red, is entirely palatable.

♟ 8 **Wine Atlas Cigales 2014** £5.97
The immediately preceding vintage of this nicely
presented Castile wine was 2011 so it's not as rounded as
its predecessor but has pleasing blackcurrant-hedgerow-
fruit savour and a little oaky vanilla, finishing very tidy –
and very Spanish; 14% alcohol.

♟ 8 **Gran Bajoz Toro 2012** £6.48
Characteristically roasted pungent black fruit, very dry
and spicy Zamora Tempranillo made, it seems to me, to
match suitably charred barbecue meats; 14% alcohol.

♟ 10 **Noster Nobilis Priorat 2013** £7.98
The same wine I top-scored in last year's edition was
just as delicious at the 2016 tasting and in the meantime
has won gold at the 2016 International Wine Challenge.
These new laurels may accelerate sales, so buy now,
particularly as Priorat had a difficult 2014 harvest and
supply might be short. Dense, gamey, lush Garnacha red
with 14.5% alcohol, madly underpriced.

♟ 8 **Extra Special El Meson Rioja Gran
Reserva 2008** £9.98
Not in the same class as last year's fabled 2005 Reserva,
but a lush raspberry-and-vanilla Rioja with its own
antique charm; 13.5% alcohol.

WHITE WINES

AUSTRALIA

8 **Extra Special Barossa Chardonnay 2015**   £5.75
Nice leesy lick in the back-flavour of this peachy-sweet-apple oaked party Chardy made with the curious addition of 3% Gewürztraminer grapes.

9 **Wine Atlas Côtes de Thau 2014**   £4.97
Lesser-known neighbour of trendy Picpoul de Pinet is tangy but complex with seagrass savour and a suggestion of grapefruit; this is last-year's wine but still fresh – look out for the 2015.

8 **Picpoul de Pinet 2015**   £5.37
Popular Mediterranean (very) dry white scores for freshness and fair price.

8 **Wine Atlas Touraine Sauvignon Blanc 2014** £5.97
Generic Loire dry white is sherbet- and gooseberry-zesty with a grassy rush of proper Sauvignon fruit; easy to like.

FRANCE

8 **Extra Special Viognier 2014**   £6.00
Last year's wine and £1 up in price, but it's notably bright and fresh, artfully balancing the grape's apricot savour with a citrus tang.

8 **Extra Special White Burgundy 2013**   £9.00
Authentic peachy Chardonnay sourced from the Côtes de Beaune as well as Chalonnais and Mâconnais; has trim citrus edge and plenty of plumpness.

8 **Haut des Janeil Gros Manseng
Sauvignon Blanc 2014**   £9.00
The Sauvignon comes out on top in spite of contributing only a fifth of the mix, but there's a lot more to this Gascon dry white; a basket of tropical-nettly-orchard flavours with plenty of interest.

WHITE WINES

9 **Extra Special Pouilly Fumé 2014** £10.00
Lavish lemon-gold colour and matching richness in the
mineral-pebbly nuanced Sauvignon from the famed
village of Pouilly-sur-Loire, facing Sancerre across the
mighty river; exciting quality from Joseph Mellot.

8 **Rully Domaine Marguerite**
Dupasquier 2012 £10.50
Sweetly ripe and minerally bright Chalonnais Chardonnay,
has a lick of the richness of oak ageing.

9 **Extra Special Chablis Domaine**
de La Levée 2014 £11.00
Well-coloured ripely perfumed textbook Chablis,
enticingly mineral and lush; from a very good vintage,
made by dependable producer Brocard.

9 **Lacheteau Vouvray 2015** £11.00
Honeyed just-off-dry Chenin Blanc from an enigmatic
Loire appellation with a very pleasing balance of
ambrosial and citrus flavours; an elegant aperitif or a
match for roast chicken; 11.5% alcohol.

9 **Sancerre Joseph Mellot 2015** £11.00
Lovely lush classic Loire Sauvignon with crystal-river
pebble freshness and citrus tang to the big, grassy
mouthfilling flavours; made by a top producer and all at
a very fair price – for Sancerre.

9 **Roversi Pecorino Terre di Chieti 2015** £5.75
This water-white Abruzzo refresher is crisply appley and
thoroughly Italian.

WHITE WINES

ITALY

🍷 **8** **Extra Special Gavi 2015** £6.00
Brassica briskness and blanched-almond richness match
up in this nice universal dry and very Italian white from
Piedmont giant Araldica.

🍷 **8** **Extra Special Pinot Grigio 2015** £6.00
Superior Trentino PG by mega-producer Cavit has smoky
savour and gentle pungency.

NEW ZEALAND

🍷 **8** **Tukituki Marlborough Sauvignon
Blanc 2014** £5.48
Inexpensive 'commerical' Kiwi Sauvignon with peapod
pong and cheery grassy flavours.

🍷 **8** **Extra Special Marlborough Sauvignon
Blanc 2015** £5.97
Absolutely reliable perennial, dry and tangy with a lick
of lushness.

🍷 **9** **Koru Sauvignon Blanc 2014** £5.98
This Nelson wine won gongs for this vintage last year but
I hadn't tasted it until 2016 when it was still aboundingly
fresh, brimming with asparagus, grapefruit, seagrass and
other Kiwi Sauvignon signatures. Terrific value at the
price – and look out for the 2015, which, natch, I haven't
tasted.

ROMANIA

🍷 **8** **Wine Atlas Feteasca Regala** £4.97
Transylvanian curiosity, quite dry but comes with a
honeysuckle perfume, meadow freshness of fruit and a
softness at the finish; 11.5% alcohol.

WHITE WINES

8 **Espartero Rioja Blanco 2015**   £4.48
Modern unoaked fresh blend of Viura and Verdejo, has crisp white fruit and a suggestion of nutty creaminess.

SPARKLING WINES

8 **Extra Special Louis Bernard Premier
Cru Champagne Brut**   £19.75
This lively house champagne is consistent good value from the brioche aroma to the lemony tang at the edge of the generous fruit.

8 **Pierre Darcys Brut Champagne**   £20.00
New champagne to me gives off a friendly aroma of apple blossom and melba toast and follows up with easy flavours; it's the kind that gets discounted and at, say, £10 would be a good buy.

8 **Extra Special Louis Bernard Vintage
Champagne Brut 2007**   £30.00
Gold appearance and mature, mellow fruit give this an unmistakably de luxe appeal.

9 **Casa Luis Cava Brut**   £4.70
The boom in Italy's foamy and frivolous Prosecco is blinding budget-minded fizz drinkers to the merits of Spain's hugely cheaper cava sparklers. This richly coloured, busily fresh and dry Catalonian confection is fun and fantastic value; 11.5% alcohol.

8 **Extra Special Marques de Portola
Cava 2013**   £7.98
Tropical-fruit aroma but crisply fresh and dry, an attractive style; 11.5% alcohol.

——The Co-operative——

The Co-operative wine tasting is always full of revelation. My local Co-op in sequestered South Somerset is a compact convenience store in which the wine offering is decidedly limited. Turning up to taste in London, I find numerous wines I have never seen before.

Some of them are terrific. Argentinian red Paz Cabernet Sauvignon Cabernet Franc 2014 at £8.49 is among my top wines of the year, and likewise an outstanding moselle, Reichsgraf von Kesselstadt Riesling Kabinett 2014 which the Co-op's buyer boldly but correctly describes as a steal at £9.99.

These and plenty more very interesting wines among those I have picked out this year are stocked in 'fewer than 1,000 stores' as the Co-op puts it, signifying really that you need to find a supermarket-sized branch to get a wide choice.

It's worth the trouble. Co-op wines have multiplied in variety in the last few years, and include progressively more own-label bottles under the headings of The Co-operative or the quirkily named 'Truly Irresistible' range. In addition, the Co-op has the most comprehensive selection of Fairtrade wines to be found anywhere.

There are still plenty of interesting individual estate wines too. Highlights this year include well-sourced red wines from France's warm south and a rare Savennières from the Loire Valley. There are distinctive wines besides from Australia and Spain, and the 'Les Pionniers' champagnes – commemorating the 19th century Pioneers of the Co-operative movement – are a perennial treat.

RED WINES

🍷 8 Finca Las Moras Barrel Select Malbec 2015 £6.99
The Co-op's note said this is unoaked, which doesn't quite chime with the label description. It does have a certain creaminess in the darkly sweet and savoury young fruit though; all rather intriguing.

**🍷 10 Paz Cabernet Sauvignon Cabernet
Franc 2014   £8.49**
Unusual 50/50 blend and Malbec-free, but this is my favourite Argentinian wine of the year. I like to imagine the San Juan sun-ripened Cab Sauv supplying the plush, smooth, blackcurrant rush of fruit and Cab Franc contributing the firm, leafy freshness and bright acidity to the lush, luxury-oaked overall texture and reach of a characterful and very satisfying whole; 14% alcohol.

🍷 8 The Hedonist Cabernet Sauvignon 2014   £9.99
You can't go wrong putting a pig on the label, and this McLaren Vale snorter certainly works for me: deep maroon colour, fleshy blackcurrant fruit of sleek oaky smoothness, easy weight and nice balance; 14% alcohol.

🍷 8 Stone Dwellers Sangiovese 2013   £12.99
Sangiovese is the grape of Chianti and here it is from Victoria State, demonstrating a sort of extra-ripe Chianti cherry-briary nose and generous matching fruit full of vivacity and depth; a very likeable special occasion Italian-red with 13.7% alcohol, maybe a match for pasta with a suitably antipodean meat sauce.

RED WINES

9 Henry's Drive Shiraz 2012   £14.99

Opaque ruby-purple Padthaway steak-supper red has a bold briar-spicy aroma and fruit with sophisticated savour and silkiness; really quite special and a reminder that Australian winemakers – Kim Jackson in this case – can closely rival their French counterparts at the upper end of the quality scale; 14.5% alcohol.

9 Ventoux Delas 2013   £6.49

Ventoux is the great mountain of Provence, as well known as the most taxing stage of the Tour de France as it is for the surrounding vineyards of the Côtes du Ventoux, but a name to look out for. Delas is a leading regional producer and this is a deliciously taut, ripe red-fruit spicy and grippy food wine at a good price.

8 Doudet-Naudin Pinot Noir 2014   £6.49

Doudet-Naudin is a Burgundy producer but here they've come up with a Pinot Noir from the Languedoc, classified a humble Vin de France, and quite delicious. It has plenty of colour (more sun in the Midi than in Beaune), lush and ripe fruit with a hint of vanilla and lots of interest. More like a red Sancerre than a Burgundy and vastly cheaper.

8 Les Crouzes Old Vines Carignan 2015   £6.49

No rough edges but plenty of garrigue and spice in this Mediterranean charmer of dark berry-fruit savour and warming ripeness.

9 Domaine des Ormes Saumur 2014   £7.49

Typical stalky mouthfeel from Cabernet Franc follows the rush of ripe redcurranty fruit in this vivid Loire Valley red – a great partner for saucy fish dishes, charcuterie, snails and other exotic menus; responds well to chilling.

RED WINES

FRANCE

🍷 8 Château Vieux Manoir 2014 £7.99

Comfortingly familiar label featuring what is indeed a very old manor house attracts the eye to this friendly Merlot-led Bordeaux. It's dark, plummy and ripe, and just escaping its tannin grip.

🍷 9 Vinsobres Les Cornuds 2013 £8.99

Vinsobres is one of the hand-picked Rhône villages granted its own appellation; this wine, from an estate, Les Cornuds, owned by the Perrin family of Châteauneuf du Pape fame, is accordingly focused and fascinating, with dark peppery savour, plushness and balance; 13.5% alcohol.

🍷 9 Château Bel Air 2012 £10.99

A 'Cru Bourgeois' estate wine from the Haut-Médoc, heartland of Bordeaux, this Cabernet Sauvignon/Merlot blend speaks fluent claret: restrained cassis fruit, slinky and minty in elegant balance, long in complexity and aftertaste; fair price too.

🍷 8 The Co-operative Châteauneuf du Pape 2014 £15.99

You pay a big premium on other Rhône village wines for the most famous of them and it's not always worth it, but this Châteauneuf from local starmakers the Perrins has it all: a maze of sumptuous black-fruit flavours strung together with silken oak and long gently spicy savour; 13.5% alcohol. This should develop for years in the bottle.

RED WINES

ITALY

9 **The Co-operative Truly Irresistible Barbera d'Asti 2013** £6.99

De luxe spin on the familiar briary-bouncing Barbera theme which owes something to the new oak barrels in which a modest proportion of this juicily delicious Piedmont wine was brought up; 14% alcohol. Very good value for this quality.

8 **The Co-operative Truly Irresistible Montepulciano d'Abruzzo 2014** £6.99

This healthily sweet and brambly version of the popular Adriatic red is pleasantly grippy with 'soft' tannin and smoothed with some oak input.

8 **Novare Valpolicella Ripasso 2013** £9.99

Good example of this reinforced version of Verona's signature red wine; the cheery cherry fruit is nicely weighted with a raisin intensity and smoothness; 13.5% alcohol.

SOUTH AFRICA

8 **The Co-operative Truly Irresistible Pinotage 2015** £6.99

The Cape's own indigenous grape is on good form in this new own-label wine showing hallmark pruny-spicy ripeness in the long black-fruit flavours; 14% alcohol.

9 **Mount Rozier Beekeeper Merlot 2014** £7.99

Affable oaked Merlot from the Stellenbosch has trim black-cherry fruit of nicely controlled sweetness and ripeness; 14% alcohol.

SPAIN

8 **Gran Vista Garnacha 2015** £7.99

A 'fruit-forward' wine from northeastern region Campo de Borja – plumply ripe and wholesome with 14% alcohol, all at a party price.

RED WINES

SPAIN

🍷 8 **Honoro Vera 2014**   £7.99

Strangely labelled with a moody and intensely Spanish portrait of a young woman (Vera?) this pure Garnacha from Calatayud is darkly savoury and substantial (14% alcohol) in its dark, plummy-blueberry spicy ripeness; I wrote down the random thought that it would go well with roast pork.

🍷 8 **Baron de Ley Rioja Reserva 2011**   £10.99

Ubiquitous Baron de Ley is among Rioja's most dependable names if not its most exciting; this is slick, silky pure Tempranillo with cassis fruit standing up well to the creamy vanilla of the oak; 13.5% alcohol.

WHITE WINES

AUSTRALIA

🍷 8 **Berton Metal Label Vermentino 2015**   £7.49

Overcome your natural antipathy for gimmicky 'metal' wine labels and try this striking lemon-gold perky vegetal-citrussy refresher.

🍷 8 **Robert Oatley Signature Series Chardonnay 2014**   £9.99

I've been hearing complaints that Aussie Chardonnays are becoming too austere as producers eschew the ripe and oaky styles of yesteryear. Well, from the Margaret River, here's a reactionary one: lush and golden with lashings of sweet-apple and peachy fruit, but with contemporary freshness and uplift.

CHILE

🍷 8 **Torres Days of Summer Muscat 2015**   £6.99

Distinctly grapy but perkily dry and fresh aperitif wine, ingeniously delicious.

WHITE WINES

8 **The Co-operative Truly Irresistible**
Picpoul de Pinet 2015 £6.99
Tangy, almost green, rendering of this trendy
Mediterranean dry white with plenty of crisp orchard fruit
and a citrus edge; sensible price.

8 **The Co-operative Truly Irresistible**
Viognier 2015 £6.99
Exotic, apricot-scented dry Pays d'Oc scores for
distinctiveness and makes an adaptable food match –
chicken, fish, creamy dishes of all kinds; ripe and sunny
with 13.5% alcohol.

9 **Savennières Domaine des Forges 2014** £10.49
This rarity from the Loire Valley is pure Chenin Blanc, for
which a quarter of the fruit was fermented in expensive
new oak barrels. The effect is a dry, brisk and enlivening
white wine with the trademark honey trace of the Chenin
and a lushness of texture that cannot fail to impress;
13.5% alcohol. Fabulously good.

8 **Saint-Véran Domaine des Valanges 2015** £10.99
Lavish Burgundy – Saint-Véran is a grand appellation
of the Mâconnais – has high colour, lush appley-peachy
Chardonnay fruit and a fine minerality with citrus
highlights.

8 **Pouilly-Fumé Domaine les Chaumes 2014** £11.99
The chalk-stream pebbly freshness of this Loire Valley
classic Sauvignon comes through loud and clear in this
very crisp and nettly posh dry wine. Instantly impressive
and the perfect match for smoked fish.

WHITE WINES

GERMANY

🍷 **8** **Eisberg Sauvignon Blanc** £3.50

One of several in the Eisberg alcohol-free wine range, this does smell like Sauvignon, complete with gooseberry greenness; in the mouth it's fruit juice, but with a certain wine consistency. Not unpleasant and for those who don't drink wine but wish to appear to be joining in, a rational product; 0.05% alcohol.

🍷 **10** **Reichsgraf von Kesselstatt Goldtröpfchen Riesling Kabinett 2014** £9.99

I'm awarding maximum points here for persistence as well as perfection in an individual wine. The Co-op has stood loyally by this delicious but esoteric Mosel wine for as long as I can remember even though it must have a very limited following. But it's a gem: racy but generous in lush-apple fruit, fresh and tangy but shot through with a thrill of honey, lipsmacking at the finish and just 8.5%. Buyer Edward Robinson says it's a steal at £9.99 'compared to the £20 price tag found elsewhere'.

N. ZEALAND

🍷 **8** **Verdicchio dei Castelli di Jesi 2015** £5.49

I thought I detected the flavour of pomelo fruit in this friendly off-dry Marches wine with likeable freshness and balance – easy drinking at an easy price.

🍷 **8** **The Co-operative Truly Irresistible Explorers Sauvignon Blanc 2015** £6.99

Steady bargain Co-op perennial has plenty of asparagus-nettle character and lush grassy freshness; it's £2 cheaper than it was two years ago.

WHITE WINES

8 The Co-operative Truly Irresistible Pinot Grigio 2014 £7.99

N. ZEALAND

Unexpected sweetness to this Marlborough variation on a Veneto theme, but it's in artful balance with good smoky orchard fruit and plenty of interest.

8 Most Wanted Albariño 2015 £7.99

SPAIN

Eye-catching brand has seaside freshness and generous typical tangy-ripe fruit.

SPARKLING WINES

9 Les Pionniers Champagne Brut £16.99

The name is French for Pioneers – in this case the Rochdale tradesmen who founded the Co-operative movement in 1844. And this is a cracking champagne, mellow and evolved with aromas and flavours commanding notions of sweet brioche yeastiness balanced by lemon tanginess; one of the top supermarket own-label sparklers.

9 Les Pionniers Champagne Brut 2006 £24.99

FRANCE

Praised here last time round and still reportedly in good supply, a richly-coloured, bready-perfumed, generous ripe wine coming round very nicely.

 The best buys at Lidl are mainly to be found in the Wine Cellar section. Launched only a couple of years ago, this is now an integral display in every store, and has featured hundreds of interesting wines along the way. New additions are made in batches several times a year and, as the Lidl wine people never tire of saying, when they're gone, they're gone.

From my standpoint it's a nightmare. I have tasted scores of new wines in the course of preparing this edition only to find that they will almost certainly have sold out by the time the book gets into print. The wines that do feature in the following pages are those I have tasted most lately, and I very much hope readers will succeed in finding them.

There are wines here too from the 'core' list, the ones you find on the standard shelving as distinct from the fancy wooden wine bins that hold the Wine Cellar bottles. Ed Adams, one of the three Masters of Wine now employed by Lidl, has tipped me the wink that there are plans for improvements to the core range, and I look forward to that.

In the meantime, keep an eye on the ever-changing Wine Cellar range. Delicious and sometimes unusual wines are to be found at very respectable prices.

Many of the numerous French wines – reds, whites, pinks and sparklers – that appear here are from the new Wine Cellar selection from France launched in the stores in October 2016. I hope very much that you will find some of them in time. 'I believe it's the best range we've introduced from France so far,' Lidl's MW Richard Bampfield told me at the last-minute tasting I attended just before this edition went to press.

For what it's worth, I think he's completely right. And even if these wines have already been snapped up by the time you're reading this, I believe there will be a lot more similarly well-chosen wines to come.

As a wine merchant, Lidl has definitely arrived.

RED WINES

⟨8⟩ Corbières Domaine Creux du Chêne 2013   £5.49
Attractively packaged textbook Mediterranean red with
a hint of toffee on the rustic hedgerow-fruit nose and lots
of vigorous briar fruit; jolly good of its kind at this price.

⟨8⟩ Malbec Pyrène 2014   £5.79
Dark maroon coaly-spicy gripper from the Comte Tolosan
has warmth and ripeness with an easy weight.

⟨8⟩ Gamay Savoie 2014   £5.99
In the glass it looks like Beaujolais, smells like Beaujolais
and tastes like something else, tighter and crunchier than
the original as made from the same Gamay grape to the
southwest of the Savoie region. Fun squishy-red-fruit
summer red to drink cool.

⟨9⟩ Alsace Pinot Noir Jean Cornelius 2015   £6.49
I fully concede that the red Pinot Noir wines of Alsace
are a bit of an oddity, but this one really should be tried.
Only just beyond rosé in colour, it's terrifically bright and
crisp in its raspberry-strawberry fruitiness, very dry and
stimulating as a food matcher (chicken, saucy fish dishes
et al) and at this price a rare bargain.

**⟨8⟩ Rhône Villages Séguret Les Terrasses
des Dentelles 2014   £6.49**
Individual Rhône appellation Séguret wine is bright in
colour and fruit showing peppery, gripping fruit; 13.5%
alcohol.

⟨8⟩ Cahors Château de Grezels 2013   £6.99
Intense and savoury Malbec from the famous appellation
of the Lot Valley has gamey ripeness and length of dark
flavour.

FRANCE

RED WINES

FRANCE

🍷 **8** **Mâcon Igé Domaine de la Bruyere 2015**   £6.99
Typically crunchy summer-red-fruit Pinot Noir of the Mâconnais (southern Burgundy), so bright and juicy it's refreshing; 13.5% alcohol.

🍷 **9** **Fleurie Collin Bourisset 2015**   £7.99
Fleurie is one of the élite 'crus' of Beaujolais and usually either expensive or dull and sometimes both. This is neither – a lovely purple gripper with proper Beaujolais bounce and a tight, defined juicy fruitiness of exciting vigour.

🍷 **8** **Hautes Côtes de Beaune Philippe de Bois d'Arnault 2014**   £8.49
From the Burgundy heartland, a big, ripe and cheerfully agricultural Pinot Noir of yeoman quality and really quite cheap for what it is.

🍷 **9** **Côtes de Castillon Château Roque Le Mayne 2014**   £8.99
Big intense purple claret from Bordeaux boondocks is cushiony-plush rather in the New World manner and none the worse for that; soothing and satisfying and already rounded out; 14% alcohol.

🍷 **8** **Arbois Clervigny 2014**   £8.99
From the Jura mountain region east of Burgundy, this is a pale, cherry-scented dry and crisply red-fruit Pinot Noir of real charm that will respond well to a little chilling; 11.5% alcohol.

RED WINES

8 Maury Domaine la Pléiade 1995 £9.99
Gloriously sweet *vin doux naturel* from the Pyrenees at
20-plus years old looks and smells like a rich oloroso
sherry but has an uplifting lightness besides; a neat
alternative to port and great value; 16% alcohol.

**8 Châteauneuf du Pape La Croix
Boidard 2015** £11.99
Young wine from the prestigious but very productive
southern Rhône appellation has a convincing kaleidoscope
of dark-fruit aromas and flavours all in a big, ripe and
smooth package; good standard Châteauneuf at a shade
under standard price; 14% alcohol.

8 Les Hauts de Pez 2012 £12.99
Christmas claret from Château La Tour de Pez in the St
Estèphe commune of Bordeaux has dense maroon colour,
sweet cassis and cedar nose – a reassuringly expensive
perfume – and slinky, lingering classic fruit.

8 Dornfelder Pfalz 2014 £4.99
Dornfelder's a recently created (well, 1950s) German
grape variety making juicy reds a bit akin to Pinot
Noir; this has denser colour than most Pinot and a nice
strawberry nose, integrated and substantial summer-ripe
fruit and a pleasing abrasion at the finish in the Italian
style. Good with pasta, risotto, fish pie, German sausage.

8 Komám Szekszárd Eszterbauer 2013 £5.99
I have faithfully copied out the weird name because this
Cabernet-Merlot blend with added regional grapes is
worth the effort: lively claret-like roast-meat red with
agreeable ripeness; 13.5% alcohol.

FRANCE

GERMANY

HUNGARY

RED WINES

ITALY

🍷 8 **Merlot Casale Ai Campo 2015**   £4.49
This party red from Veneto is pale, cherry-bright and
dry with Beaujolais-like weight and bounce; I'd drink it
chilled.

🍷 9 **Teroldego Rotaliano Riserva
Superiore 2012**   £5.79
Dark, rounded mountain red from Teroldego grapes
grown at Rotaliano in the sub-Alpine Alto Adige with
alluring blackcurrant perfume and matching juicy fruit
with gripping intensity and proper Italian abrasion; a
distinct bargain.

🍷 8 **Chianti Classico Fortezza dei Colli 2012**   £6.99
Nicely packaged year-round genuine wine, deep maroon,
slinkily fruity in the prescribed manner and gently grippy.

🍷 8 **Valpolicella Ripasso Classico
Superiore 2012**   £7.99
This style of Valpolicella, made with the addition of
concentrated grape must, is catching on, and here's a
good-value one, raspberry ripe, satisfyingly weighted,
clean and pleasantly abrasive; 13.5% alcohol.

🍷 8 **Barolo 2011**   £9.99
Permanent fixture doesn't seem to sell very fast in my local
Lidl but it has the sort of gamey savour it should have, and
lots of fruits-of-the-forest complexity; 14.5% alcohol.

SPAIN

🍷 9 **Barrica España Barceliño 2014**   £4.99
Juicy Catalan party red feels creamily oaked but is perkily
piquant with blackcurrant fruit; 13.5% alcohol.

RED WINES

SPAIN

🍷 **8**   **Baturrica Gran Reserva 2009**   **£4.99**
New (to me) core-range Tarragona has middleweight blackcurranty fruit from Tempranillo and Cabernet Sauvignon and evident but not-overwhelming oak influence; safe buy at this price.

🍷 **8**   **Cepa Lebrel Rioja Reserva 2011**   **£5.49**
In the core range, a consistent creamily cassis-rich Rioja wonderful in last year's 2010 vintage; perhaps this one will mellow further but it's already an impressive wine at the price. Don't be put off by the murky, grey and near-illegible label; 13.5% aclohol.

🍷 **9**   **Priorat Vinya Carles 2012**   **£5.79**
Dense purple-black colour leads the way into this intense cassis fruit red from the cult Priorat region west of Barcelona; it's smooth and rich but brisk at the edge; complex and lingering with what I've written down as 'custardy' oak, by which I mean well; 14% alcohol.

🍷 **9**   **Ribera del Duero Altos de Tamaron 2013**   **£5.99**
Worthy follow-up to last year's brilliant 2012 vintage, this pure Tempranillo delivers sunburnt-ripe fruit veiled in creamy oak and minty sleekness; pedigree wine at a giveaway price; 13.5% alcohol.

🍷 **8**   **Rioja Reserva Soligamar 2011**   **£8.99**
Still young-tasting and darkly brooding smoothly oaked expensively upholstered Rioja that should repay keeping a year or two; 14% alcohol.

PINK WINES

FRANCE

🍷 8 **Rosé Coteaux d'Aix en Provence
Albert Pineaud 2015**   £4.99
Pale onion-skin colour, floral nose and dry, even elegant, style to this delicate pink from an appellation that's usually pricier.

🍷 8 **Costières de Nîmes Le Rosé de
Madame S 2015**   £5.49
Dignified onion-skin colour and delicate meadow-strawberry perfume give this fresh, dry Rhône pink a wholesome appeal.

🍷 8 **Rosé d'Anjou 2015**   £5.49
Bright, tangy and full of summery soft red fruit, a likeable Loire dry pink with a crafty lick of sweetness; 10.5% alcohol.

🍷 8 **Minervois Rosé Pierre Fontaine 2015**   £5.99
Pale salmon colour and gently sweet red fruit in this fresh 'n' dry Mediterranean party pink.

SPAIN

🍷 8 **Rioja Rosado Cepa Lebrel 2015**   £4.99
Smoked salmon colour, palpable summer-soft-fruit of perky freshness, dry and brisk; 13.5% alcohol.

WHITE WINES

8 **Grüner Veltliner Terraces Domäne Wachau 2015**   £7.99
Nice pearly whiff on this full-flavoured dry varietal plump with sweet-pear fruit finishing crisply tangy.

8 **Sauvignon Blanc Caprice de Berticot 2015**   £4.99
Straight Midi sauvignon, clean, grassy and crisp – and cheap.

10 **Côtes de Gascogne Le Heron 2015**   £5.99
Outstanding richly coloured and honeyed off-dry wine from the esoteric Gros Manseng grape grown in Atlantic Gascony; freshness, plumpness and peachy ripeness get equal emphasis and the sum of these parts adds up to a very seductive entirety with a genteel 11.5% alcohol. An attention-grabbing aperitif or a versatile match for saucy fish or poultry, even elaborate salads.

8 **Apremont Savoie 2015**   £5.99
Surprising floral-sweet aroma on this trendy après-ski wine leads into brassica-crisp fresh flavours in a distinctively dry style that is exotic and fun; 11.5% alcohol.

8 **Touraine Sauvignon Blanc Les Celliers du Bellay 2015**   £5.99
This easy-going, gently grassy Loire refresher has delicacy and balance and just 10.5% alcohol.

8 **Alsace Riesling Ernest Wein 2015**   £6.49
Brisk smoky-limey Riesling in the authentic Alsace style at an attractive price – a safe bet.

WHITE WINES

8 **Picpoul de Pinet Mascavinae 2015** £6.99
More fruit and less brittleness than some other brands of this popular Mediterranean shellfish-matcher, I liked this for its softness.

9 **Domaine des Petits Quarts Coteaux
du Layon 2014** £7.49
Luscious Loire dessert wine is honeyed but clean-edged, beautifully balanced; as well as a pud matcher it makes a fine aperitif with a nut, a peach or a Bath Oliver; 11.5% alcohol and a rare bargain.

9 **Entre-Deux-Mers Château Marjosse 2013** £7.99
Rich colour to this mature dry white Bordeaux is matched by the fullness and exotic nature of the lush fruit; a class act made, I believe, from the traditional Bordeaux white-wine blend of Sauvignon Blanc with Semillon.

8 **Pacherenc du Vic-Bilh Tradition 2011** £7.99
I can't see this tongue-twister flying off the shelves, but it's a delectable dessert wine nonetheless, made from a lot of strange grapes late-harvested in the Madiran district of Gascony, including the Gros Manseng featured in the fabulous Le Heron wine described above. Gold in colour and ambrosially honeyed but all in sublime balance.

8 **Reuilly Domaine du Chêne Vert 2015** £8.99
Loire rarity is all Sauvignon Blanc giving off an alluring pungent blossomy pong and delivering flavours encompassing gooseberry, asparagus and much besides; a fascinating dry refresher.

WHITE WINES

FRANCE

🍷 **9** **Rully Blanchard de Cordambles 2015** **£9.99**
Gorgeous Chalonnais (Burgundy) Chardonnay is luscious but mineral bright with depths of sweet-apple and pineapple savour; Rully may not have the grandeur of Meursault or Puligny-Montrachet but the better wines, like this one, have great natural appeal – and affordability.

🍷 **9** **Chablis 1er Cru Jean Desvignes 2015** **£11.99**
Lidl's buyers are good at Chablis. This is the real thing, poised confidently between steeliness and rich ripeness in the unique Chablis style, a very natural wine.

🍷 **8** **Alsace Grand Cru Gewürztraminer JP Muller 2013** **£11.99**
Individual-vineyard wine has trademark lychee and roses aroma and an unexpected lightness in weight, but it's long in exotic, smoky fruit flavours. I think this will repay keeping for a few years.

🍷 **8** **Châteauneuf du Pape Blanc 2015** **£11.99**
Show-off's wine; plush with exotic fruits including apricot, mango, pineapple and other less-identifiable varieties, but it's quite dry and brisk as well as lingeringly lush; price seems fair; 14% alcohol.

WHITE WINES

9 **Riesling Pfalz 2015** £4.99
A very plainly packaged Rhine that well illustrates the magic appeal of Riesling raciness and grapiness; a very superior party just-dry white with just 8.5% alcohol and a lot of character. Why does Lidl do so few German wines?

8 **Cantina Valle Isarco Müller Thurgau 2015** £6.99
From the sub-Alpine Alto Adige, an aromatic but flinty-dry mountain refresher of real charm.

8 **Grüner Veltliner Alto Adige 2015** £7.49
Mysteriously popular smoky-spicy dry white more usually produced in Austria works very nicely in this sub-Alpine manifestation; nice assertive match with Asian dishes; 13.5% alcohol.

8 **Gewürztraminer Südtirol Alto Adige 2015** £7.99
Signature lychee perfume ushers in a tangy version of the familiar rich Alsace original; this sub-Alpine Italian spin has lively merits of its own; 13.5% alcohol.

8 **Ribeiro Casal do Rio 2015** £4.79
Pineapple ripeness and lemon zest form the flavour formula for this inexpensive Galician dry white at a keen price; 11% alcohol.

9 **Rioja Blanco Joven Conde de Altava 2015** £4.99
Up-to-the-minute very dry white making a virtue of freshness but still showing the lush character of the constituent Viura grape, finishing with a lively citrus twang.

WHITE WINES

8 **Rueda Blanco Visigodo 2015** £4.99
The name's a reminder of Spain's Visigoth past and the pleasing Verdejo/Viura blend in this brisk dry party white is a reminder of how far Spanish dry white wines have come in more recent times.

8 **Albariño Sentidiño Rias Baixas 2015** £5.99
The wine's not quite as seaside bright as the blue marine label might suggest but it has fresh appeal and scores for price.

8 **Rueda Verdejo Alteza 2015** £6.49
Voguish variety Verdejo makes a pleasing balance between tropical ripeness and sea-breezy tang; good of its kind.

8 **Vinho Branco Palmela Paço do Bispo 2015** £4.99
Dry but exotic vegetal/herbaceous Setubal wine has distinctive appeal; a natural seafood matcher.

SPARKLING WINES

9 **Champagne Bissinger Brut 37.5cl** £6.99
Fresh and lively champers in that rare but oh-so-useful measure, the half bottle; a bargain.

9 **Clairette de Die Cuvée Elégance** £6.99
Discreetly honeyed, fresh-straw-evoking sparkly refresher from Drôme in the Rhône bounds Tiggerishly from the glass, prompting Richard Bampfield to say 'If there's one wine that brings a smile to my face it's Clairette de Die'. This one, I think, is a 'Tradition' blend of Clairette and Muscat grapes and just 7.5% alcohol.

SPARKLING WINES

9 Crémant d'Alsace Weiber Blanc
de Blancs Riesling £7.99
Well-coloured and creamily sparkling regional speciality
shows apple crispness and fruitiness in nifty balance;
11.5% alcohol.

8 Champagne Comte de Senneval Blanc
de Noirs Brut £14.99
The lemon tang at the opening will wake you up to the
mellow biscuity depths in this fine, lively sparkler.

8 Champagne Bissinger Brut Rosé £15.99
Powder-puff pink and perky with strawberry aromas and
fruit, this succeeds in tasting like pink champagne, and
it's down in price from last year.

8 Rheingau Riesling Herzog von
Nassau 2013 £6.99
Convincingly effervescent Rhine wine tastes exactly as
you might expect – racy apple-fresh nuanced Riesling
fruit all a-sparkle; a curiosity and a likeable one.

8 Moscato Gavioli £5.99
Ambitious bottle reminiscent of Perrier Jouët Belle
Epoque, reveals a pale, sweet and gently *spumante*
confection for sipping with birthday cake; 9.5% alcohol.

Majestic

 Majestic's new range of own-label wines is a definite success. Under the sensible and appropriate heading Definition, the range 'captures the quintessential qualities of the world's greatest wine styles', says the blurb, 'with a little help from some of the world's greatest winemakers'.

There are 14 Definition wines, so far, and most of them appear here. They are fair value, especially when bought at the discounts always on offer at Majestic. These continue in their accustomed profusion and complexity even though the retailer has finally abandoned its lifetime policy of enforcing a minimum purchase. All the wines are now offered at two prices: one for purchases of fewer than six bottles at a time, the other for larger purchases, any mix.

In the stores and online, therefore, you'll find tandem prices on everything, single bottle or Mix Six. At it applies universally, I've decided to list both the single-bottle purchase price and the Mix Six price for all the wines recommended in the following pages. Thus for example £11.99/£9.99 means £11.99 if you're buying five or fewer bottles, any mix, and £9.99 if you're buying more than that, any mix. The discounts vary broadly from 10 to 20 per cent. Very many of the wines, please note, will also be offered individually on varying further discounts through the year.

These deals apply equally on the Majestic website.

In last year's edition I blithered on a bit about the dramatic changes that had lately taken place at the company. Majestic had bought the unconventional online merchant Naked Wines (est 2008), whose founder Rowan Gormley then somehow emerged as Majestic's new chief executive.

How would it turn out, I wondered. Well, Majestic in 2016 has announced sales have risen over the previous year by a barely believable 41 per cent. So that's all right then. Profits, however, are down 30 per cent. Which is not so good.

Am I worried? I was until I attended the press tasting. Whatever's going on in the board room, the people who source the wines and work in the 200-plus branches are clearly beavering away. There are lots of terrific wines – and new wines, too – and there's value as well as interest. Britain's biggest high-street merchant, included in this guide from the start because I can't bear to leave it out, looks to be in good heart.

RED WINES

ARGENTINA

🍷 **8** **Definition Malbec 2015** £10.99/£8.99

Big red grabs you by the tastebuds with pleasantly puckering pure plum and spice flavours in the muscular leather-scented Mendoza Malbec style; 14.5% alcohol.

🍷 **9** **Ben Marco Malbec 2013** £14.99/£12.99

Lovely spicy savour to the baked black fruit in this ritzy ripe and rich Mendoza de luxe varietal; it's expensive but a relishable example of what Argentina is capable of; 14% alcohol.

AUSTRALIA

🍷 **9** **The Astronomer Shiraz 2014** £6.99/£5.99

Loopy label illustration and chat but you'll warm at once to this De Bortoli bargain. The bouncing blackberry fruit has heft and ripeness, spice and sweet mint and maintains perfect trim; 14% alcohol.

FRANCE

🍷 **8** **Lirac Domaine des Garrigues 2014** £9.99/£8.99

Neighbour to Châteauneuf du Pape and forever compared to it, this one is vivid with long red fruits, nicely intense and ripe; could do with more time; 14% alcohol.

🍷 **8** **Definition Côtes du Rhône 2015** £10.99/£8.99

This big but not blowsy superior sort of CdR from Plan de Dieu appellation (I believe) is a good choice in this 'defining' role because you get indicative spicy dark fruit and sun-baked ripeness; 14.5% alcohol.

🍷 **9** **Bourgogne Pinot Noir Nicolas Potel 2013** £11.99/£9.99

Alluring sweet black cherry nose on this Côte d'Or generic Pinot is followed up by corresponding wholesome juicy fruit; Nicolas Potel is a name to look out for in Burgundy.

RED WINES

9 **Definition Claret 2012** £11.99/£9.99
They've gone for a Montagne St Emilion, one of the
satellite appellations of the famous Libournais town,
for this soupy-looking and imposing ripe and generous
mainly Merlot wine. It's 'modern' claret with upfront
fruit and slick juiciness already nicely evolved; 13.5%
alcohol.

9 **Crozes-Hermitage L'Hermitage
2013** £11.99/£10.49
From the excellent Cave de Tain co-operative of growers
on the famed Hermitage hill of the northern Rhône,
an immediately appealing dark and pure Syrah with
purple forest-fruit density and cling; lovely now, and will
develop.

8 **Beaujolais Lantignié Louis
Jadot 2015** £11.99/£10.49
Rather pricy but impressive deep mauve young wine with
firm juicy-raspberry fruit and proper Beaujolais character;
13.5% alcohol.

8 **Château La Négly La Côte 2015** £12.99/£9.99
From the always-interesting La Clape zone of the
Languedoc a toasty black-fruit garrigue red with warm
spice and Mediterranean ripeness; 13.5% alcohol. Note
the generous Mix Six discount.

9 **Château Moncets 2009** £14.99/£12.99
From the right-bank Bordeaux appellation of Lalande
de Pomerol here's a lovely forthcoming claret from a
legendary vintage; poised black fruit evoking coffee,
cedarwood and vanilla and much besides; 13.5% alcohol.
A treat and not overpriced.

Majestic

FRANCE

RED WINES

ITALY

🍷 **8** **Corolla Nero d'Avola 2013** £7.99/£6.99

Straight, deep purple blackberry, crisply defined pasta red from the home of the excellent Nero d'Avola grape of Sicily.

🍷 **8** **De Forville Dolcetto d'Alba 2015** £9.99/£8.99

The De Forville dynasty has been making wine in Piedmont since the 1860s and Majestic has been selling them just as long, I guess. Silly me, but this producer deserves the continuity; this briary forest-fruit red is deliciously poised and balanced, juicy and refreshing; an ideal pasta partner; 13.5% alcohol.

🍷 **8** **Definition Chianti Classico 2013** £11.99/£9.99

It fits the profile – cherry/blackberry ripe with agreeable abrasion, lively and fresh; 13.5% alcohol.

NEW ZEALAND

🍷 **8** **Definition Pinot Noir 2014** £13.99/£11.99

From admirable Saint Clair estate in Marlborough, a full, ripe raspberry-strawberry Pinot with hallmark Kiwi mint and sleekness; nicely polished wine; 13.5% alcohol.

🍷 **8** **Coney Pizzicato Pinot Noir 2014** £15.99/£13.99

This is your earthy style of Kiwi Pinot Noir, in spite of the curious highfalutin name; from Pinot Noir central, Martinborough, it's seductively ripe, silky and satisfying; 14% alcohol.

PORTUGAL

🍷 **9** **Ramos Reserva 2014** £7.99/£6.99

Classic Alentejo wine, distinctively dark and savoury with red fruits, cloves and minty depths; good sinewy mouthfeel and long flavours; 14% alcohol. As with so many undervalued Portuguese red wines, a genuine bargain.

RED WINES

ROMANIA

🍷 9 **Incanta Pinot Noir 2015**   £6.99/£5.99

Evoking the kind of strawberry syrup that gets poured over ice cream, this purple glugger turns out to be more than a mere confection: firmly gripping and balanced Pinot of wholesome style and satisfying weight, it charms.

S. AFRICA

🍷 9 **Capaia Merlot Cabernet 2011**   £9.99/£8.99

Blood-red Bordeaux-type blend from Philadelphia in the Western Cape delivering depth, intensity and distance of flavour in an awesomely ripe package; almost a caricature of oak-matured claret but brilliantly in balance and a bit of a bargain; 14% alcohol.

SPAIN

🍷 10 **Definition Rioja Reserva 2009**   £11.99/£9.99

I fully realise that Rioja is a safe refuge. You always have a pretty fair idea of what to expect for your money. In this case, you get a lot more. This is a dark, dark wine just browning a tad at the edge with a saucy cassis-vanilla nose and gorgeous mellow but pin-bright fruit with a fim but friendly tannic clasp. It's 95% Tempranillo, 14% alcohol, and drinking very well from a famously ripe Rioja vintage. For what it is, it's jolly cheap.

🍷 8 **Matsu El Viejo 2014**   £21.00/£18.90

Premium wine from Toro has a disturbing photo-portrait label (very Spanish) and comes from very viejo (old) Tinta de Toro (Tempranillo) vines averaging 110 years of age. It's brilliantly dark, lush, rich and nuanced and 15% alcohol.

RED WINES

USA

🍷 8 **Decoy Zinfandel 2013** £22.00/£19.80
Endearing duck label denotes a wine from the famous Duckhorn Vineyards in California's Sonoma County. It's an absolute quacker: ripe but taut dark fruit with a marzipan trace and ideal balance; 13.9% alcohol.

PINK WINES

ARGENTINA

🍷 8 **Hey Malbec Rosé 2016** £11.99/£9.99
Delicate pink colour reveals a positively pink-tasting wine bouncing with red-berry fruits and finishing just short of bone-dry with a nice citrus edge.

🍷 8 **Cuvée de Richard Rosé 2015** £6.99/£5.99
Petal pink party Pays d'Hérault is crisply dry with cheery whiffs of strawberry and a lemon tang at the edge.

🍷 8 **Domaine La Chautarde Rosé 2015** £8.99/£7.99
Provencal pink has an attractive smoked salmon colour, delicate and crisp summer-soft-fruit flavours and a dry, citrus finish.

FRANCE

🍷 8 **Leon Perdigal Côtes du Rhône Rosé 2015** £8.99/£7.99
Strong colour, masses of bright fruit and crisp delivery in this Grenache-based ripely stimulating dry wine; a rosé of interest.

🍷 8 **Miraval Rosé 2015** £17.99/£15.99
In the celebrated ownership of Hollywood stars Mr and Mrs Brad Pitt, this expensive Provencal pink has a bright coral colour, delicate summery perfume and frankly delicious and refreshing pink flavour, very fresh and assured.

Majestic

PINK WINES

FRANCE

♈ 8 **AIX Rosé 2015 Magnum** £22.00/£19.80
Party-piece bumper bottle in clear glass to show off this Provence rosé's pink bloom to great effect, and the wine does not disappoint: typical elegant dry fruit with strawberry-lemon perfume.

WHITE WINES

♈ 8 **Anakena El Viajero Sauvignon Blanc 2015** £8.99/£6.99
Lingering fresh asparagussy Leyda Valley wine, has typical Chilean ripeness and balance.

CHILE

♈ 9 **Santa Ema Sauvignon Gris 2015** £8.99/£7.99
Sauvignon Gris is related to the better-known Blanc version but is said to have more intense flavours. This Leyda Valley (Pacific coast) wine gives a clue: there's grassy freshness and green fruits, but ripe tropical notes too; 13.5% alcohol. Tricky to deconstruct, easy to like.

♈ 8 **Mâcon-Villages Domaine Des Maréchaudes 2014** £9.99/£8.49
Mineral peachy-leesy typical Mâcon Chardonnay full of the ripeness of a famously fine vintage.

FRANCE

♈ 10 **Vouvray Domaine des Aubuisières Cuvée de Perruches 2014** £9.99/£8.99
This Chenin Blanc from the Loire deserves as much attention as the region's Sauvignon Blanc or for that matter Burgundy's Chardonnay and Germany's Riesling. This is a gorgeous just off-dry Chenin with a limey tang and a vaulting freshness shot through with floral-nectar highlights. Lavish and uplifting you could drink it as an elegant aperitif or with just about any menu from smoked

WHITE WINES

fish to roast pork or anything exotic and spicy. It's cheap for what it is.

9 A Casetta 2015 £9.99/£8.99

It's pure Vermentino from Corsica, and so-called after the casetta, the small stone house of the vineyard. The wine is a sunny holiday refresher of exceptional charm bursting with orchardy/mango/melon fruit, tangy fresh and friendly; 11.5% alcohol. Stands out from the crowd.

8 Kuhlmann-Platz Riesling 2015 £9.99/£8.99

It looks German, but it's from Alsace, where they make French wines from German grape varieties. This childishly labelled gem is a grown-up mineral-smoky-limey Riesling in the classic Alsace manner, dry, exotic and distinctively delicious.

9 Definition Chardonnay 2014 £11.99/£9.99

From Limoux in the Aude, a fine florally perfumed peachy pure Chardonnay, very full but neatly trimmed with citrus acidity and finishing dry. A brave choice for the new own-label range – much easier just to look to the Mâconnais – and a successful one; 13.5% alcohol.

8 Côtes du Rhône Blanc Pierre-Henri Morel 2015 £11.99/£9.99

Rare-ish white from Grenache Blanc, Roussanne and Viognier, flush with exotic and orchard fruit, spicy ripe and quite dry; in the style of white Châteaneuf-du-Pape and, as such, fair value; 14% alcohol.

FRANCE

WHITE WINES

8 **Laurent Miquel Albariño 2015**   £12.99/£10.99
From Lagrasse in Corbières this artful pastiche of the Albariño of Galicia replicates the tangy zing offering apple-limey freshness and thought-provoking complexity; a conversation piece.

8 **Definition Chablis 2015**   £13.99/£12.49
Steely start to this very proper Chablis by Louis Moreau morphs pleasingly into long greeny-gold minerality and even a saucy hint of creaminess.

9 **L'Hospitalet Grand Vin Blanc 2014**   £22.00/£17.00
Opulent gold oak-plumped dry wine from cult Languedoc enclave La Clape marries exotic white- and stone-fruit flavours to uplifting freshness; 14% alcohol. It tastes even more expensive than the price indicates.

8 **Sancerre Comte Lafon 2014**   £27.50/£24.75
From grand centuries-old Loire producer Ladoucette a lavish and mineral Sauvignon of great character. Sancerre fanatics should try it.

8 **Peter & Ulrich Dry Riesling 2015**   £11.99/£9.99
Fine floral-grapy aroma on this Zeltingen moselle and fresh sweet-apple fruit to follow; it's fermented out (12% alcohol) but grapy dry rather than dry dry.

8 **Cortese Araldica 2015**   £6.99/£5.99
Piedmont varietal by local giant Araldica is a convincing shadow of trendy Gavi (also made from Cortese), dry and briskly crisp with hints of brassica and blanched almonds in an attractive package; 11.5% alcohol.

WHITE WINES

ITALY

 8 **Tasca Regaleali Bianco di Sicilia 2015** £8.99/£7.99

Zesty seaside fresh island wine from a bewildering array of local grapes plus Chardonnay is distinctively likeable.

8 **Definition Pinot Grigio 2015** £9.99/£8.99

Definitely from the respectable end of the PG spectrum, this Venezia Giulia dry white is properly bright with suggestions of smoke and spice.

NEW ZEALAND

9 **Mud House Pinot Gris 2015** £8.99/£7.99

This is PG in what was once known as the Alsace style – full, pungent, smoky and brilliant with spicy foods – and it's drier and crisper than some Alsace counterparts I've tasted; 13.5% alcohol and really rather good value.

8 **Definition Sauvignon Blanc 2015** £10.99/£8.99

Asparagus is to the fore in the brightly green nose of this friendly Marlborough grassy-fresh varietal; very straight wine that should appeal to Kiwi Sauvignon purists.

8 **Waimea Estate Grüner Veltliner 2015** £11.99/£9.99

This might be in short supply as the Waimea in Nelson has only three rows of Grüner vines. Snap this up: it's ripely delicious with herby-spicy overtones to the orchard fruit, brassica-fresh and adaptable to many menus; 13.5% alcohol.

SLOVENIA

8 **Krasno Sauvignon Blanc Ribolla 2015** £7.99/£6.99

Let's hear it for Slovenia! This is a full-flavoured Sauvignon in a very ripe, almost rancio, style that's nevertheless stimulatingly fresh and lively; grabs the attention and a good fish match for sardines and the like.

Majestic

WHITE WINES

SPAIN

🍷 8 **Carro de Santa Maria 2015** £7.99/£6.99
Breezy blend of Verdejo with Viura has apple zest and a discreet Rioja Blanca-type richness from the Viura; artfully – and organically – produced.

🍷 8 **Pazos De Ulloa Ribeiro 2015** £7.99/£6.99
Brisk and perky Galicia dry wine from Palomino, the sherry grape, and Muscat-like Torrontes, has an underlying grapy juiciness all its own; 11.2% alcohol.

SPARKLING WINES

ENGLAND

🍷 8 **Nyetimber Rosé** £44.99/£39.99
Quality pink fizz, from Chardonnay and Pinot Noir grapes grown in West Sussex, you get salmon colour, bright strawberry-tinged fresh young fruitiness all in a fine flow of effervescence; at the price definitely one for patriotic thirsts.

FRANCE

🍷 7 **Le Berceau Frisante Piquepoul
Chardonnay** £11.99/£8.99
It looks like cynical exploitation of the twin vogues for Picpoul de Pinet and dodgy fizz, but this Jean-Paul Mas Mediterranean production is an improvement on prosecco, with sweetish but balanced orchard fruit.

🍷 8 **Prima Perla Reserve Brut** £12.99/£9.99
Another Mas-production (see Le Berceau above) but this time an all-Chardonnay 'méthode traditionelle' bottle-fermented sparkler with bakery aromas, ripe-apple fruit and crispness; refreshing and fun.

ITALY

🍷 7 **Definition Prosecco Brut** £12.99/£9.99
It's got a bit of sweetness in spite of the 'Brut' tag and typical peary fruit emerging from the froth; 11% alcohol. It's fine of its kind but surely overpriced.

—Marks & Spencer—

There are always so many delightful M&S wines I wish to describe that my usual problem is knowing where to start. This year, however, is different. The annual tasting laid on by M&S for the wine media was unexpectedly interrupted by a fire drill. We all had to evacuate the building.

In fairness, I had already tried lots of newsworthy wines. South American reds were showing very well, and Italian whites, and Spain seems to be strengthening at M&S, just as it is at most other retailers. But I did not get to all the white wines by any means and missed the rosés altogether.

Under normal circumstances, I would have waited with the vast crowd of evacuees outside M&S's London HQ until the all-clear was given and we could return to our task. But not on this occasion. It was my birthday and I was needed elsewhere.

There was, however, consolation. Charles Metcalfe, star of the London musical stage as well as a distinguished wine critic, upon hearing it was a special day for me, sang *Happy Birthday* in operatic mode. And Oz Clarke, no shrinking violet either, gave me a congratulatory kiss.

Whether or not Marks & Spencer choose to stage their tasting on my birthday again next year, I very much hope they will invite me in spite of my jumping ship on this occasion. And it might be a good idea for someone in the management to advise the wine department well in advance of any future planned fire drills. Possibly M&S staff themselves are accustomed to these contingencies, but members of the media, always pressed for time, are likely to take a less-accommodating view of an evacuation order. And we are, of course, notoriously indiscreet about even the tiniest corporate failings.

Finally, I urge M&S shoppers who have not already done so to take a look at the wine offerings online. The range is far wider than in most of the stores, and the discounts are far more numerous and various than you'll find on the shelves. All the wines are sold online by the six-bottle case, which I suppose is what triggers the reductions, and the price cuts are up to 50 per cent.

RED WINES

ARGENTINA

🍷 8 **Butcher's Block Bonarda Malbec 2015** £6.50
Bonarda, originally an Italian grape, comprises 70% of
this blend, so don't expect the meaty Malbec character
suggested by the brand name. It's a firm but friendly
brambly glugger with a nice bounce of blackberry fruit.

🍷 8 **Nieto Senetiner Bonarda Malbec 2015** £9.00
Red-blooded Mendoza blend has sinew and smoothness
to its dark fruit; well-judged weight and balance.

🍷 8 **Craft 3 Malbec 2015** £10.00
There is an unexpected leafy freshness apparent in this
hearty, gamey and authentically Argentinian pure Malbec
at 13.5% alcohol. Distinctive and satisfying and, I note
to my surprise, made by Gerd Stepp of Palatio fame (see
Germany below).

AUSTRALIA

🍷 8 **Burra Brook Cabernet Sauvignon 2015** £8.50
'Cheerful healthy sweet ripe amply generous and briskly
trimmed nice normal wine' is what I wrote in stream-of-
consciousness fashion before realising I was tasting an
M&S regular I have not previously liked very much. But
never mind that, I liked it now; 14% alcohol.

🍷 8 **The Islander Kangaroo Island Shiraz 2015** £12.50
Australia's third-largest island, which appears to be
covered in vineyards, produces this long, slinky varietal
with liquorice and spice in the considerable depths of the
dark berry flavour with 14.5% alcohol. Made by Jacques
Lurton, scion of a famous Bordeaux dynasty.

🍷 9 **Coonawarra Gable Cabernet 2014** £16.00
Blood-red old-fashioned gripper by top regional producer
Wynns, gorgeously intense and savoury yet elegant and
balanced; 13.5% alcohol.

RED WINES

BOLIVIA

🍷 8 **Campos de Solana Tannat Malbec 2015** £11.00
From Santa Ana in the Andean foothills of southern Bolivia, an entirely new wine (and wine region) to me, this blend is a little disconcertingly ethereal in weight but full of vivid black fruit discreetly spiced and oaked with 14% alcohol.

CHILE

🍷 9 **Ancestral Old Vine Cinsault Pais Carignan 2014** £12.00
From the Chilean outpost of Catalonian wizard Miguel Torres, this uncommon blend deliciously illustrates the magic of so many Torres wines. It's a big-hearted, plummy-spicy number with intense ripeness and an elusive pruny-sweet, even bitter-chocolate core to the flavour that lifts it from marvellous to memorable; 14.5% alcohol.

FRANCE

🍷 8 **Domaine de la Clairière 2015** £5.50
Winsome Mediterranean Merlot is juicy with bright brambly black fruit, finishing nicely taut.

🍷 9 **Domaine Mandeville Shiraz 2015** £8.50
Besides grinding my teeth at the use of Australian 'Shiraz' to describe the grape known in its native France as Syrah I have to concede this boldly purple Pays d'Oc has inviting minty-raspberry aromas and a lot of darkly gripping spicily savoury black fruit.

🍷 8 **Domaine de Rosette Chinon 2014** £9.00
Wild briar and redcurrant fruit in this highly distinctive Loire Cabernet Franc is stranded with leafy green notes to make a fresh and stimulating wine that responds well to chilling.

RED WINES

8 **Henry Fessy Coteaux Bourguignons 2015**   **£9.00**
Henry Fessy is a famous Beaujolais producer so it's no surprise this generic Burgundy is made with the Beaujolais grape Gamay. It's juicy, slurpy and delicious; 13.5% alcohol.

FRANCE

9 **Château Les Croisille Cahors 2013**   **£10.50**
Once known for semi-mythical 'black' wine Cahors is now closer in style to Bordeaux but with Malbec (known locally as Cot) in the principal role. This is a sleek but unoaked pure Malbec with savoury blackberry spicy dark fruit in its own style.

9 **Domaine Bunan Bandol 2011**   **£16.00**
From a fashionable resort on the Côte d'Azur, a lush blackberry-pie-with-cream, slinky and minty de luxe red largely from Mourvèdre grapes from the appellation's premier producer, Domaine Bunan; it's rounding out nicely but will develop for years more; please note 15% alcohol.

GERMANY

10 **Palataia Pinot Noir 2014**   **£10.50**
Stark new label on this perennial favourite from Rheinpfalz producer Gerd Stepp, a former M&S staffer, will I hope attract more attention to a fabulous wine. Everything about it is bright and polished: the jewel-like colour, the pinging Pinot perfume of ripe summer soft fruits, the mineral-pure, cherry-ripe fruit craftily enhanced with time in oak and the perfect crispness at the finish; 13.5% alcohol. Easily my top Pinot from anywhere at this price.

RED WINES

8 Reggiano Rosso 2015 £6.00
Made from Lambrusco grapes, a sweet-cherry but quite
dry midweight Emilia-Romagna red with a shade of nutty
creaminess; like a firm Valpolicella but more interesting.

8 La Fortezza Merlot 2015 £7.00
Sicilian spin on the ripe black-cherry Merlot theme has
the warm herby-spiciness that often marks the island's
reds and a welcome textural richness.

8 Teroldego Rotaliano 2015 £8.00
Quirky darkly savoury wine from sub-Alpine Trentino
region has a trademark stalky-leafy streak in the crunchy
blackberry fruit; smoothed out with oak contact it's a
versatile food match.

8 La Masca Barbera d'Alba 2014 £10.00
Barbera wines are usually brambly, bouncy and light-
hearted; here's a more serious one, long-oak-aged to
give toasty smoothness to the juicy fruit and gravitas all
round; 13.5% alcohol.

8 Brolio Chianti Classico Riserva 2011 £30.00
I can't help calling this a Chianti Grand Cru Classé
because it is so reminiscent of the grand Bordeaux style.
It even includes a portion of Cabernet and Merlot along
with the main Chianti grape Sangiovese. It's gorgeous,
already rounded and mellow with oaky-smoky-cedary
elements in the regal cassis and cherry fruit; 14% alcohol.

8 Six Hats Fairtrade Shiraz 2015 £8.00
Abounding with plump ripe fruit with discreet vanilla
and spice, a big but balanced typical Cape savoury food
red of worthy origin and real charm; 14.5% alcohol.

ITALY

S. AFRICA

RED WINES

🍷 8 **Cornelia Swartland Red 2014**   £10.00
Big friendly blend of Shiraz, Grenache and Cinsaut has well-knit, gamey relish and controlled ripeness; well-made, it seems to me; 13.5% alcohol.

🍷 8 **Las Falleras Tinto 2015**   £5.00
Bright Utiel-Requena wine has perky cherry and red fruit juiciness that resolves in a neat, dry finish; good value.

🍷 8 **Raso de la Cruz Red 2015**   £7.00
Summertime red of easy weight and focused gently spicy fruit should respond well to chilling.

🍷 8 **D'Aragon Old Vine Cariñena 2015**   £8.00
Deep maroon colour to this intense and plummy, brambly oaked Cariñena wine from the Cariñena region; healthy, vigorous and 13.5% alcohol.

🍷 8 **Castillo de Los Templarios Mencia 2015**   £9.50
Mencia is a rather scarce black grape variety native to the northwestern region of Galicia, whence this sleek and distinctive red combining a smooth (but oak-free) mouthfeel with spicy blackberry bite to the fruit; made by the co-operative at Bierzo, a typically cleverly sought-out M&S wine; 13.5% alcohol.

🍷 8 **Artadi Alava Vineyards Tempranillo 2012** £13.00
The Basque region of Alava neighbours Rioja but is less well-known for its wines. Well, not known at all. So try this darkly ripe and intense Rioja-type red and wonder: it's opulent and gripping, in need of more bottle-age and 14% alcohol – and another clever M&S discovery.

RED WINES

URUGUAY

10 Pisano Cisplatino Tannat 2015 £9.00
I gave the 2014 vintage maximum points last year, and I'm not about to downgrade the 2015, an excitingly dark and mysterious monster with a ripe intense plummy nose, wholesome purple gripping damson-plum fruit and beautifully judged weight with 13.5% alcohol. The Tannat grape, a native of Gascony, is Uruguay's flagship variety, and rightly so.

USA

8 New York State Red 2015 £8.00
From America's oldest winery, established on Long Island in 1839, an irresistible juicy summer red from a blend of mystery Baco Noir grapes with Cabernet Sauvignon and Cabernet Franc.

8 Underwood Pinot Noir 2014 £13.00
Pale but very attractive Oregon pure varietal has mouthfilling sweet but poised emphatic Pinot fruit all in finely judged balance; distinctive style.

WHITE WINES

CHILE

8 Cascara Casablanca Chardonnay 2015 £9.00
Effusively ripe and complex basket-of-fruits dry wine from Pacific-side vineyards has a joyful freshness that's hard to resist; 13.5% alcohol.

FRANCE

8 Gers 2015 £5.50
My friend Mario, who lived there, says that Gers is pronounced 'jerss' and makes wine to which he is averss. But here's a likeable one, dry pure Colombard, cool and lemony with crisp orchard fruit, healthy, refreshing – and cheap.

WHITE WINES

8 **White Burgundy 2015** £9.50
From the formidable co-op at Buxy in the Chalonnais a nicely wrought appley-peachy Chardonnay with a twitch of creamy oak and long lush fruit; proper generic burgundy worthy of confidence.

8 **Mâcon La Roche Vineuse 2014** £13.00
Lavish gold colour and matching rich lushness of stone fruit in this special southern Burgundy made, I believe, without oak contact. It has a natural wholesomeness all its own.

8 **Pierre de Préhy Chablis 2014** £14.50
This is an ordinary Chablis AC and not a Premier Cru, but it justifies the price by offering classic characteristics of green-gold colour, aromas of flint and minty sharp apple and luscious mineral Chardonnay fruit; unmistakably good Chablis by estimable Domaine Brocard.

8 **Darting Estate Dürkheimer Riesling 2015** £10.00
Gold-coloured and just slightly prickly, this is an unusually richly ripe QbA wine from the Pfalz, with raciness and minerality working well alongside the sweet-apple fruit; 14% alcohol.

10 **Bianco Vino da Tavola 2015** £5.00
Humble white table wine it might be but this dry Trebbiano from Emilia-Romagna is very pleasingly fresh and lively with a naughty kiss of sweet-blanched-almond amid the perky orchard fruit; an outstanding bargain.

FRANCE

GERMANY

ITALY

WHITE WINES

8 **Garganega Pinot Grigio 2015** £8.00
It would be my favourite Pinot Grigio of the year were
this Veneto dry white not in fact constituted of only 15%
PG grapes. The rest is Garganega, the grape of Soave, but
it's a very nifty mix, fresh, herbaceous, fascinating and a
versatile food matcher.

8 **Alta Luna Gewürztraminer 2015** £9.00
Don't expect the big pungent Alsace style from this sub-
Alpine Gewürz: you do get the expected lychee and roses
perfume and fruit but not the sweetness and spice – a
fascinating fresh spin on an exotic theme.

10 **Ascheri Langhe Arneis 2014** £13.00
To explain: Ascheri is a posh Piedmont wine producer,
Langhe is an exquisite hill zone renowned for its vineyards
and a UNESCO World Heritage site to boot, and Arneis
is an esoteric local grape variety that in this case makes
a magnificently good, sleek spearmint-piquant grassy-
nettly dry white with a streak of tangy citrus somehow
shot through with a creamy-nutty richness.

8 **Tapada de Villar Vinho Verde 2015** £8.50
Quite a prickle in this dry 'green wine' from Portugal's
northwest, harvested early to retain acidity and maximise
freshness; this feels less sweetened than most commercial
brands and has keen green fruit; 10.5% alcohol.

8 **Raso de la Cruz White 2015** £7.00
Notably tangy dry Macabeo-based wine from Cariñena,
a landbound region southwest of Rioja nevertheless has
seaside zing and freshness; likeable and distinctive.

WHITE WINES

SPAIN

🍷 8 **Jordi Miró Garnacha Blanca 2015**   £9.00
Self-assured varietal from Terra Alta in the far southwest packs both crisp green zest and peachy ripeness and 13.5% alcohol. The label avers it is a match for barbecued chicken but I'd employ it to give life to salad dishes.

USA

🍷 8 **New York State White 2015**   £8.00
Fun soft but not flabby blend mainly of Riesling and Sauvignon has plenty of white orchard fruit and definition.

SPARKLING WINES

ITALY

🍷 8 **Ferrari Brut**   £20.00
The best sparkling wine of Italy, putting prosecco firmly in its place, this pure-Chardonnay bottle-fermented fizz has the yeasty aromas and arch style of champagne. The fizz started up in 1902, the famed car marque not till 1929.

Morrisons

Morrisons kindly sent me a few wines to try after they staged a tasting to which I was not invited. I bought some from my nearest branch, and have therefore been able to try a modest fraction of the range.

Thus the truncated nature of this section. I liked some of the wines I did get to sample and suspect things might be looking up at Morrisons, wine-wise. The main strength is their 'Signature' own-label range. These are so-called because they are endorsed with a reproduction of the signature of William Morrison, who founded Morrisons in 1888, at the foot of the label. The word 'Signature' itself does not appear. I just thought I should clear that up.

Besides the stores, in which I do rather wonder at the reasoning behind the arrangement of the wine sections, Morrisons sells wine online. The Morrisons Wine Cellar website helpfully lists all the wines on discount up front, so promo-addicts needn't scroll any further down than necessary. I had thought to buy my sampling wines online but discovered Morrisons don't deliver to my postcode in Somerset. Ho hum.

Among the wines I have managed to taste, the standouts were both Chablis. I have unhesitatingly awarded maximum points to the Signature Premier Cru 2013 wine from the La Chablisienne co-operative at £15.00. And I am now feeling rather guilty about giving only 9 points to its stablemate Signature Chablis 2014 at £10. I award these scores at the time of tasting and am forsworn never to adjust them subsequently, but in this case I need to point out that these two wines are in fact equally outstanding.

Rumours of a tie-up between Morrisons and Amazon were authenticated in 2016 and we can look forward to all sorts of Morrisons food and drink going online alongside the books and CDs in the future. I can barely contain my excitement.

RED WINES

ARGENTINA

🍷 **8** **Signature Malbec 2014** **£8.00**
First taste evokes redcurrant jelly but this is not a 'jammy' wine; it's a roasty-toasty blackly savoury intensely ripe and luxury-oaked light-heavyweight that will certainly make a match with roast lamb; 13.5% alcohol.

AUSTRALIA

🍷 **9** **Australian Red Wine** **£3.75**
Non-vintage party red has at least eight different constituent grapes, bright ruby colour, a perky briar nose and a whole basket of juicy black-fruit flavours with a trace of marzipan sweet softness. At this price, it's brilliant.

🍷 **8** **Beaujolais 2014** **£5.00**
Specially selected from the Beaujolais vineyards, it says on the label, and that's it, provenance-wise, but this is a bright, squishy-juicy summer red in correct style to drink cool.

FRANCE

🍷 **9** **Signature Côtes du Rhône Villages 2015** **£6.50**
Nice one – lively defined typical spicy red fruits with ideal food-matching tannic abrasion that also keeps the ripeness in balance; you know it's well-made, and the price is very fair.

🍷 **8** **Signature Languedoc 2013** **£7.00**
From one third each Syrah, Grenache and Mourvèdre, one of several Mediterranean wines made for Morrisons by leading producer (and former French rugby legend) Gérard Bertrand, this is suitably muscular and robust with good heft; 14% alcohol.

RED WINES

FRANCE

🍷 8 **Signature Red Burgundy 2014** £8.00
A small measure of Gamay gives the 85% Pinot Noir in this a bit of bounce, which might just be the making of this juicy raspberry-cherry charmer.

ITALY

🍷 8 **Signature Sangiovese Superiore 2013** £6.00
From the Chianti grape but not from Chianti country, this Romagna red has cherry-red-fruit ripeness and creamy texture in the Chianti mode and a plumskin grip of tannin; a likeable Italian oddity; 13.5% alcohol.

🍷 8 **Signature Valpolicella Ripasso 2014** £7.50
Trace of Amarone bitterness in the bright cherry aroma of this souped-up Verona red gives extra intrigue to the darkness and savour of the fruit. Good rich-meaty-dish matcher with its grippy dry finish; 13.5% alcohol.

PORTUGAL

🍷 5 **Douro 2014** £8.00
Disappointing, even weedy imitation of what should be a flagship table wine from the Port country.

SPAIN

🍷 8 **Signature Rioja Reserva 2011** £7.00
Cheap wine tasted cheap on first opening but next day it had bloomed and mellowed and seemed really good for the money. This is an advantage of buying the wine and tasting it when you feel like it, including the day after – which of course I had to do in this case as Morrisons did not include me among those invited to their wine tasting.

🍷 8 **Reino de la Viña Rioja Reserva 2011** £10.00
Smartly presented modern Rioja by giant Bodegas Muriel has warmly rounded but bright blackcurrant fruit and a well-judged heft; 13.5% alcohol. I got my bottle on promo for £7 – about the right price.

WHITE WINES

FRANCE

9 **Signature Alsace Pinot Gris 2014** £8.25
Gold colour and an affecting pungent smoky-citrussy
nose give a keen welcome to this unusually brisk and
zesty Alsace PG. The exotic flavours, featuring mango,
stone fruit and gentle spice, are profiled with delightful
clarity. OK, I'm rambling, but it really is a terrific wine
of its kind.

9 **Signature Chablis 2014** £10.00
Made in a great Chablis vintage, this immediately
impresses with the trademark gunflint aroma followed
up by crisp but leesy shell-bright Chardonnay fruit and
generous ripeness; from ace co-op La Chablisienne.

10 **Signature Chablis 1er Cru 2013** £15.00
The beguiling richness in this grand wine owes something
to the fermentation of one fifth of the juice in oak casks,
but lush fruit ripeness and the natural properties of the
Chardonnay grape have no doubt played their part too.
The effect is a beautifully poised classic Chablis that
refreshes, stimulates and comforts. Top wine from La
Chablisienne co-operative.

ITALY

8 **Signature Fiano 2015** £6.00
Brisk almost bracing entry into the flavour of this dry
Sicilian varietal gives way to fleshy grapefruit and melon
flavours with a lemon twang; refreshing and interesting.

8 **Signature Soave Classico 2015** £6.25
The green hue that glimmers in the gold colour seems
to translate into a grassy lushness in this prickly-fresh
Verona dry wine.

WHITE WINES

Morrisons

ITALY

8 **Signature Godello 2014** £8.00
Eye-catchingly packaged Galician varietal makes a lively marriage of seaside freshness with exotic tropical fruit.

8 **Signature Pecorino 2015** £8.00
Grapefruit and lime both crop up in the grassy fruit of this pleasing Abruzzo dry white adorned with a label artistically depicting a sheep in a nod to the Pecorino grape's ovine Latin name.

SOUTH AFRICA

8 **Morrisons Chenin Blanc 2016** £4.00
Healthy nectarine-grapefruit refresher with a honey strand will stand up to most menus including spicy dishes; jolly good and jolly cheap.

8 **Signature Chenin Blanc 2015** £7.00
Brassica fresh and crisp but with the trademark Chenin trace of sweet-nut ripeness, a sunny, balanced white wine to match exotic menus; 13.5% alcohol.

SPAIN

9 **Signature Canto Real Rueda Verdejo 2014** £6.00
This was fantastically good when I bought it in June 2016, bright with exotic brassica aromas and flavours with lush seagrass freshness and a combo citrus tang, but sneakily unchallenging in its acidity. The 2015 is coming soon but wasn't available in the stores for me to try for this edition. If you find the 2014, pounce; if you find the 2015, risk it.

8 **Signature Albariño 2015** £8.00
Relatively austere rendering of the familiar Atlantic-fresh and tangy dry white does also show fleeting notions of apple, peach and blanched almonds; lives up to the snazzy label.

Sainsbury's

Sainsbury's is so utterly consistent in the excellence of its wine range that I wish to give thanks. They have the best-designed, least-confusing in-store wine sections, and bravely haven't bothered to venture into dedicated online wine retailing even though all their larger competitors have done so – with very mixed success, I gather.

It's the flagship 'Taste the Difference' wines that lead the way. Three-quarters of all those I've picked out this year are from the range. Included are my favourite Australian red of the year made at the nation's oldest wine estate, Château Tanunda, and a terrific Touraine Sauvignon Blanc.

The TTD brand also extends to some outstandingly good and good-value sherries which I cannot commend too highly. These include not just the 12-Year-Old Amontillado and Fino I have mentioned here, but others I have recommended before, in particular the bargain-priced (£5.50) Bledn of Amontillado Medium Dry Sherry and Dry Manzanilla Superior Sherry from the Winemakers' Selection range.

Other highlights include a new (2013) vintage of perennial favourite red from the Loire Valley Chinon du Colombier which wins maximum points in succession to the 10-scoring 2012. Most Loire reds, including this one, are made entirely from the Cabernet Franc and have a uniquely fresh, leafy style I am convinced deserves more attention than it customarily receives.

Sainsbury's continues to offer regular discounts on wine. They have dropped what I had thought was the permanent deal of five per cent off any six bottles bought together, but several times a year reduce prices across the entire range by a full 25 per cent. This invariably includes wines already on individual promotion – and there are always plenty of those – which can cut the price by as much as a half.

I am quite happy to confess that I buy lots of wine at Sainsbury's in these promotions. Very good wines at very low prices are one of life's consolations. Thank you, Sainsbury's, for that too.

RED WINES

ARGENTINA

🍷 **8** **Taste the Difference Morador Malbec 2015 £8.00**
Big, ripe pruny Fairtrade item from Argentina's signature black grape; 13.5% alcohol.

🍷 **9** **Clos de Los Siete 2013** **£15.00**
Deluxe Bordeaux-variety blend (mainly Malbec) from premier French winemaker Michel Rolland is sumptuous and complex with echoes of grand claret and an indisputable elegance; 14.5% alcohol.

AUSTRALIA

🍷 **10** **Taste the Difference Château Tanunda**
Barossa Cabernet Merlot 2014 **£10.00**
Blood-red, toasty black-fruit-nosed Aussie 'claret' from the nation's oldest château (1890, no less) delivers antipodean heft with clever Bordeaux-like balance, featuring cassis and cedar, prunes and silk and much besides, all at a realistic price with 14.5% alcohol; hugely enjoyable.

CHILE

🍷 **8** **Taste the Difference Aconcagua**
Chilean Pinot Noir 2015 **£8.00**
Pale but substantially flavoured versatile food matcher brims with cherry-strawberry ripeness all in healthy balance; 14% alcohol.

🍷 **8** **Taste the Difference Chilean Cabernet**
Sauvignon Merlot 2014 **£8.00**
Errazuriz-made, oak-aged Bordeaux-style blend has dramatic darkness and density but well-judged heft and balance; satisfyingly savoury black-fruit formula to match meat or starchy dishes; 13.5% alcohol.

RED WINES

8 **Château David 2014** £6.50
Humble Bordeaux Supérieur delivers plenty of blackcurrant and briar in a convincingly claret-like medium; no oak but quite sleek – and cheap.

10 **Domaine du Colombier Chinon 2013** £7.00
Outstanding perennial from the Loire is lush, pure Cabernet Franc, intense with red fruits and firm in its poise. A unique red-wine style, ripe and leafy, to suit difficult menus, you can chill this to truly refreshing effect.

9 **Taste the Difference Languedoc Rouge 2015** £7.00
Very consistent dark, spicy and savoury Mediterranean winter red has a nicely adminstered smoothness from oak contact; look out for regular discounts; 13.5% alcohol.

8 **Taste the Difference Côtes du Rhône Villages 2014** £7.00
Made by dependable Chapoutier winery, a briskly peppery and juicy midweight purple quencher of lively vigour; 13.5% alcohol.

7 **Taste the Difference Pic St Loup 2014** £8.00
Lighter vintage than of memory, which to date has been fond of this distinctive Languedoc Syrah-Grenache blend from a sought-after mountain appellation. Maybe wait for the 2015.

7 **Château la Tulipe de la Garde 2014** £10.00
Enthusiastically marketed oak-matured single-estate Bordeaux is OK in this vintage with vigorous Merlot-dominated character, maybe a little under-ripe.

RED WINES

8 **Antonin Rodet Burgundy Pinot Noir 2014 £11.00**
Good hit of intense sunny ripe Pinot from this well-coloured authentic Burgundy in a slinky medium part-wrought in new oak; winemaker is called Racine.

9 **Taste the Difference Gigondas 2013** **£13.00**
This is upmarket Côtes du Rhône, marrying the crunch and spice of the generic tradition with the plush, dark texture of the ripest black fruit matured in oak; a lovely luxury wine to keep for a year or two to maximise the savour; 13.5% alcohol.

9 **St Joseph Les Challeys-Delas 2014** **£15.00**
St Joseph is an extended appellation of the northern Rhône nothing like as grand as Cornas, Côte Rôtie or Hermitage but sometimes working similar magic with the Syrah grape; this one is bright and defined in its spiced red fruitiness and slinky with warm savoury ripeness; an experience. Fine Wine section.

8 **Taste the Difference Rheinhessen**
Pinot Noir 2015 **£7.00**
Pale but purposeful ripe cherry-raspberry summer red to drink with big-flavoured fish dishes or other difficult menus; wholesome and closer in style to Chalonnais than to usual German pinots.

9 **Winemakers' Selection Montepulciano**
D'Abruzzo 2014 **£6.00**
I think this is the same wine as Asda's Extra Special edition at £5.00 but my note says I like it better – 'sweetness under control, perky and briary' – so maybe it's different. Probably just me.

FRANCE

GERMANY

ITALY

RED WINES

Sainsbury's

ITALY

🍷 **8** Taste the Difference Aglianico
del Vulture 2011 £8.00

There's a whiff of brimstone (and no, I don't mean clumsily employed antibacterial sulphur from the winemaking process) in the peppery-chocolate black darkness of this relishable meaty red from the volcanic landscape of Vulture in Basilicata. In short, delicious.

🍷 **9** Taste the Difference Barbaresco 2013 £9.00

Already turning orange-brown at the edge of the limpid ruby colour, this has a delicate tea and roses perfume followed up by deliciously slinky and developed red-berry fruit in the inimitable style of Piedmont's Nebbiolo grape; this is cheap for a decent Barbaresco and a fine introduction to the genre; 13.5% alcohol.

SPAIN

🍷 **7** Real Compañía de Vinos Tempranillo 2010 £6.50

Among the cheapest wines I bought all year, at a promo price of £3.56, this Castilla VdT is a Rioja-style party red, light but not flabby and with a vanilla oak sheen.

🍷 **8** Era Costana Rioja Crianza 2013 £6.75

A bright young thing by Rioja standards, this has perky cassis fruit, evident vanilla from oak contact and a rounded style; 13.5% alcohol.

🍷 **8** Taste the Difference Douro 2014 £8.00

From admirable Port house (and table wine specialist) Quinta do Crasto, a deep, deep purple, slick (but unoaked, I believe), minty and darkly savoury wine very obviously Port-country in origin; almost raisiny-ripe and quite delicious; seems cheap; 14% alcohol.

RED WINES

8 Taste the Difference Graciano 2014 £8.00

Vino de la Tierra de Castilla from little-known Graciano grape has a distinct mauve tint to the colour, bright red-fruit aromas and a juicy, mulberry-minty summer-soft-fruit glugginess.

10 Taste the Difference Cepa Alegro
Rioja Reserva 2010 £10.00

Smooth-as-silk, creamy-vanilla mature Rioja of the most insinuating kind is nonetheless bright with piquant blackcurrant juiciness; its secret might be the unusual blend of Tempranillo with 15% Graciano. At the price I paid, £5.25 in an extravagant promotion, the Rioja bargain of the year.

8 Taste the Difference Priorat 2013 £10.00

Muscular rather than stringy dark Garnacha-based heavyweight from Priorat region of Catalonia has rustic black-fruit relish and plenty of toasty ripeness; I'd keep it for years to see how it evolves, but it's already hard to resist; 14.5% alcohol.

PINK WINES

8 **Winemakers' Selection Côtes du Rhône Rosé 2015** £6.00
Economy pink, wholesomely fresh with recognisable CdR fruit and a keen dry edge.

FRANCE

8 **Les Caillottes Sancerre Rosé 2015** £13.00
You need to like rosé a lot to spend thirteen quid on one bottle but if you must, this is probably the one. It's pure Pinot Noir from the famous Loire appellation, a limpid salmon pink hue, strawberry perfume but very dry, pebbly even, with a long rush of bright fruit that tastes, well, pink.

SPAIN

8 **Taste the Difference Viñedos Barrihuelo Rioja Rosado 2015** £8.00
Boldly coloured blend of Tempranillo and Garnacha diluted with Viura is certainly a proper Rioja and has plenty of cassis and crispness; will stand up to most menus, even paella; 13.5% alcohol.

WHITE WINES

AUSTRIA

8 **Taste the Difference Grüner Veltliner 2015** £8.00
Crisp but exotic mix of zest and ripeness from grapes that have to dig deep into the chalky soil of the Traisental and somehow produce suitably mineral flavours; needs trying.

FRANCE

8 **Winemakers' Selection Côtes de Gascogne 2015** £5.00
Simple, crisply fresh dry Atlantic party wine from workhorse Colombard grapes plus a measure of Sauvignon; 11.5% alcohol.

WHITE WINES

8 Taste the Difference Bordeaux
Sauvignon Blanc 2015 £7.00
Bordeaux Sauvignon is deservedly back in fashion: this one lures you in with flares of lemon, lime and nettles, a rush of bristling grassy fruit. It's made by a man called Paul Oui.

8 Taste the Difference Muscadet Sèvre &
Maine sur lie 2015 £7.00
Enthusiasm for the bracing delights of Muscadet is clearly evergreen even though so many of these estuarial Loire bone-dry wines are harsh and sharp. This one is rather gentle and friendly with the right tang, grassiness and lemon edge in easy-drinking mode.

9 Taste the Difference Touraine
Sauvignon Blanc 2015 £8.00
Eight quid might seem a bit steep for a generic Loire Sauvignon, but I liked this better than the TTD Sancerre, priced at £14. It's from the Vouvray area, known for Chenin Blanc, but an eye-openingly racy-limey-flinty yet lushly ripe Sauvignon of standout style.

8 Picpoul de Pinet Ormarine 2015 £8.00
Faintest spritz contributes extra zest to this pungent Mediterranean oyster-matcher; nice twist of lemon at the edge.

8 Taste the Difference Bourgogne
Aligoté 2015 £8.00
Burgundy's only non-Chardonnay white wine can be sharp but this one's ripe and lushly cabbagey (in a good way) with long mineral flavours – comparable to Spain's trendy Albariño, it occurs to me.

WHITE WINES

8 Taste the Difference Languedoc
Blanc 2015 £8.00
Generous mélange of orchard and exotic white fruits in this consistent ripe and refreshing dry wine by Mediterranean maestro Jean-Claude Mas; versatile food matcher and frequently discounted.

9 Taste the Difference Chablis 2015 £10.00
My pick of the several Chablis on the day, this is an assertive leesy unoaked flinty-dry wine very much in the archetypal Chablis style with a defined lemon edge.

8 Taste the Difference Pouilly-Fumé 2015 £12.00
Maybe a bit new in the bottle when I tasted it in March 2016 but showing promise: nettles and seagrass in the lushly ripe style of Sauvignon from this prestige Loire appellation; 13.5% alcohol.

8 Taste the Difference Gavi 2015 £4.00
Almondy-rich and freshly bright with a citrus twang, a distinctive and distinctly Italian dry aperitif wine from Piedmont.

8 Taste the Difference Soave Classico 2015 £7.00
A grown-up example of the Veronese staple, crisply brisk, almost ascetic, but with the trademark green glitter in the colour and almondy richness at the finish; suits creamy pasta dishes as well as simple fish.

8 Taste the Difference Pinot Grigio 2015 £8.00
From the Alto Adige and correspondingly fresh it gets assistance from 15% Chardonnay – a novel twist.

WHITE WINES

NEW ZEALAND

🍷 8 **Taste the Difference Awatere Valley Riesling 2015** £8.00

Almost green in its freshness, this limey food wine has lashings of Riesling raciness along with a grapy charge; attention-grabbing food wine from top-performing winery Yealands.

🍷 8 **Taste the Difference Coolwater Bay Sauvignon Blanc 2015** £8.00

From a carbon-neutral winery, it says here, an appropriately pure-tasting basket of Kiwi Sauvignon aromas and flavours: gooseberry and lemon, asparagus and seagrass.

🍷 8 **Taste the Difference River Block Sauvignon Blanc 2015** £10.00

Wildly aromatic green-grass-gooseberry-passion-fruit 'single vineyard' Marlborough refresher has sherbet zing and long classic flavours; not cheap but I got my bottle in a promo for under £6.

🍷 8 **Cloudy Bay Sauvignon Blanc 2015** £21.00

Icon from the Fine Wine section is on good form, very nice to taste it. Nettles and gooseberries jump from the glass at you and the fruit is long and luxuriant, made with a small portion of oak-fermented must for added richness amid all that Kiwi Sauvignon zing; 13.5% alcohol.

PORTUGAL

🍷 8 **Winemakers' Selection Vinho Verde** £5.00

The fleeting fizziness is detected even on the nose in the pear-like but really quite dry fruit of this delicate aperitif; 9% alcohol.

WHITE WINES

S. AFRICA

8 **Zalze Reserve Chenin Blanc 2015** £10.00
Ripe, honeyed but essentially dry, elegant and stimulating
aperitif wine with oak contact; would match tricky menus
too; grows on you.

SPAIN

8 Taste the Difference **Albariño 2015** £8.00
As seaside fresh as you might expect from its source, the
Rias Baixas in Atlantic Galicia, and an intriguing brassica
lushness.

8 Taste the Difference **Godello 2015** £8.00
Godello's the new go-to grape from Spain; in this one
from Bierzo you get a floral perfume and flavours juggling
stone fruit and white nuts with an appley crispness; jolly,
interesting dry wine with a ripe 13.5% alcohol.

8 Taste the Difference **Viñedos
Barrihuelo Rioja Blanco 2015** £8.00
Straight unoaked pure Viura has bright crispness
cunningly counterpointed by nutty ripeness; nice example
of the modern white-Rioja style.

FORTIFIED WINES

SPAIN

9 Taste the Difference **12-Year-Old
Amontillado Sherry** £8.00
Superb toasty-figgy perfectly (but not austerely) dry
sherry of ravishing colour and stimulating piquancy; a
gift at this price; 19% alcohol.

9 Taste the Difference **Fino Sherry** £8.00
Piercingly pungent, tangy but nutty and intensely
flavoursome bone-dry pale sherry to drink thoroughly
chilled; made by Lustau; 15% alcohol.

SPARKLING WINES

**10 Winemakers' Selection Blanc
de Noir Champagne Brut** £20.00

Must declare an interest: I buy this on promotion and keep it for years so it evolves into a mellow miracle of maturity; even straight off the shelf it has a beguiling bakery aroma, long, full fruit flowing through the eager bubbles and a spirit-lifting freshness of style.

**9 Winemakers' Selection Champagne
Brut Rosé** £23.00

Attractive bronze-pink colour, full-on strawberry scent and style with a twangy but not fierce acidity, this stands out among the pink champagnes of the year; I preferred it to the Veuve Clicquot Rosé tasted alongside at £45.

8 Moët & Chandon Nectar Champagne £35.00

This is 'dessert' champagne but not really much sweeter than Moët's own brut NV (which I do find a bit sweet); seductive aroma, lush richness and nifty balance should lure in affluent fizz lovers who like a bit of mellow.

8 Taste the Difference Sparkling Pinot Rosé £10.00

Prosecco by another name made pink by mixing Pinots Bianco and Nero, and I liked its party-frock colour, strawberry nose and perky persistent fizz; fruity just short of sweet; 11% alcohol.

**7 Taste the Difference Conegliano
Prosecco Superiore 2015** £10.00

Very pale, pretty fizzy, slightly peary fruit and quite dry; presumably an identikit prosecco, but not cheap, which surely it should be; 10.5% alcohol.

SPARKLING WINES

SPAIN

🍷 **7** **Codorniu Cuvée Barcelona Brut** £13.00
I liked this but thought it a bit pricy: full, generous softly ripe and busily fizzy cava of beguiling charm easily pips prosecco's weedy allure; 11.5% alcohol.

Tesco

 It looks like Armageddon in the Tesco wine department. As the behemoth strives to reinvent itself as a viable enterprise, the wine range has been dramatically reduced in number and diversity – and even, here and there, in price. Alone among the retailers featured in this book, Tesco did not put on a tasting for the press in the first half of 2016. I bought all the wines described in the following pages. Thanks a lot, Tesco.

The relatively small number of wines reviewed is not entirely accounted for by my parsimony. The choice on the shelves really has dwindled.

I understand that Tesco seeks to 'simplify' its wine range, so it seems a curiosity that in the process of doing so it has dumped its entire entry-level range under the 'Tesco Simply' banner. I recommended half a dozen of these modest bargains in last year's edition and will miss them. Also excised, I gather, has been the 'Vineyards' range which I'll admit had rather escaped my notice.

As to the wines that have escaped the axe and made it into this space, I must mention Finest Ribero del Duero 2011 from Spain as a deserved winner of maximum points and Finest Côtes de Gascogne Blanc 2015 from Atlantic France which came very close. These are reminders of what Tesco has long been capable of and give me hope for the future.

Oddly enough, one of the last news items I received from Tesco before their press office fell silent was that 'Tesco is now focused on offering customers more stable prices and simpler promotions, and everyday low pricing on our own-label range.' From this I assume that discounts, to date a major wine-department strategy, are coming to an end along with everything else.

But it can't be that bad. Tesco must surely be working on its rebirth as a wine retailer. Not long ago, and for all I know even today, Tesco has been the source of one third of all the wine we drink at home in Britain. Who knows what surprises the stricken giant might have in store for us?

RED WINES

CHILE

9 **Finest Las Lomitas Merlot 2015** £6.00
Juicy and friendly blackcurrant plumply ripe varietal has 14% alcohol and wholesome balance.

9 **Tesco Beaujolais** £4.50
I do miss the decorative floral label of old, but this plain-wrapper non-vintage everyday glugger is still by a mile the best and best-value generic Beaujolais; wild Gamay perfume, juicy-fresh typical lively fruit and a crisp texture.

8 **Tesco Côtes du Rhône Villages 2015** £5.00
Big rangy callow hedgerow red of recognisable character in a commendably plain wrapper; 13.5% alcohol.

FRANCE

9 **Finest Côtes Catalanes Grenache 2014** £6.00
Stalwart perennial in what I fear is its last vintage on Tesco's shelves. It's wholesome, brambly-spicy and substantial and if you reseal (it's a screwcap) and try again the next day it actually seems to round out and mellow. Buy now before it is extinguished.

9 **St Joseph Cuvée d'Automne 2012** £14.99
Still on shelf from last year, this gamey-spicy northern Rhône pure Syrah seems to be benefiting materially from time in the bottle; substantial, silky and satisfying and very often on promotion – I've seen it for as little as £7.00; can't think why it hasn't sold faster.

ITALY

7 **Finest Chianti Riserva 2013** £6.00
From ubiquitous giant Piccini, a just-recognisable Chianti of cheery fruitfulness.

RED WINES

ITALY

🍷 **8** Barbera d'Alba Lo Zoccolaio Suculé 2012 £8.00
Big sweetly briary and mellow Piedmont smoothie has lush spice, discreet oak creaminess and a decent grip of tannin tidying up the long, savoury finish; 14% alcohol.

🍷 **8** Rocca Alata Valpolicella Ripasso 2013 £9.00
Fine cherry-ripe and agreeably abrasive Verona red has red-fruit and sweet-nut savour; good of its kind and a nice match for creamy pasta or risotto.

N. ZEALAND

🍷 **1** Finest Marlborough Pinot Noir 2015 £7.00
This was awful – unbalanced and synthetic-tasting, devoid of life; might have been a bad bottle.

SPAIN

🍷 **10** Finest Ribera del Duero 2011 £7.00
I am a complete sucker for the mature, creamy-toffee cassis style of this classy red-meat wine with its silky eucalyptus mintiness and sleek top-claret-like heft; a rare treat at an unusually low price for the grand Ribera del Duero appellation; 14% alcohol.

🍷 **7** Finest Viña del Cura Rioja Reserva 2011 £8.00
Out goes old favourite Viña de Mara and in comes this lookalike Finest own-brand from the same source, Baron de Ley. 13.5% alcohol. This is a decent effort with easy blackcurrant fruit and a memory of vanilla.

WHITE WINES

AUSTRALIA

🍷 8 **Finest Tingleup Riesling 2015** £8.00
Assertive limey dry perennial in fine racy condition in this new vintage which, at £8, is a fifth cheaper than previous ones at no cost to quality or interest.

🍷 8 **Tim Adams Clare Valley Riesling 2014** £9.75
Consistent limey dry food wine (Asian/spicy/poultry) of assertive racy fruit showing the gamut of citrus flavours including grapefruit and lemon besides; 11.5% alcohol.

🍷 9 **Finest Côtes de Gascogne Gros Manseng
Sauvignon Blanc 2015** £6.00
Nifty mix of aromatic and exotic Manseng with twangy Sauvignon from the Atlantic vineyards of Gascony delivers a distinctive and satisfying zesty-fresh food wine (fish, poultry, rice dishes, creamy pasta, you name it) with a modest 11.5% alcohol.

FRANCE

🍷 9 **Finest Alsace Gewürztraminer 2014** £7.50
'Fresh and crisp' the newly restyled label declares on this hardy perennial with confident irrelevance. 'Perfumed and fascinating' might be a better sell for the acutely distinctive Alsace Gewürz style and this generously coloured and aromatic wine is a good one, bright and spicy, exotic and notably free of the cloy of residual sugar that mars too many of the generic wines. Good one.

🍷 7 **Tesco White Burgundy 2015** £8.00
It takes you on a tour of fruit sensations from the sweet-apple nose through peaches and pear-drop fruit to a finish in which lemon and grapefruit both figure; in the round, interesting if not exciting.

WHITE WINES

NEW ZEALAND

🍷 8 **Wairau Cove Chardonnay 2015** £6.50
I was surprised at the weight and fullness of this
inexpensive brand – lots of sweet-apple ripeness, notions
of cinnamon and spearmint, all in the best Kiwi tradition.

🍷 6 **Brancott Estate Sauvignon Blanc 2015** £8.99
'Celebrating our 40th Anniversary' trumpets the
commemorative badging on this, the first mass-market
Kiwi Sauvignon, back in the day known as Montana. But
it's not the revelation it was. Bright crisp start but there's
a sweetness that speaks big brand and it lacks edge.

FORTIFIED WINES

PORTUGAL

🍷 9 **Finest 10-Year-Old Tawny Port** £12.00
Symington-made wood-aged wine is terrific at this price:
colour is ruby not tawny but you get the mellow minty
richness unique to the style and lots of figgy-white-
nut savour in the plump body of the wine; ardent but
reassuringly mature; 20% alcohol. Back label rightly
points out that this makes a fine aperitif straight from
the fridge.

SPARKLING WINES

FRANCE

🍷 9 **Finest Premier Cru Champagne Brut** £18.00
Consistent Chardonnay-based perennial from reportedly
superior vineyards certainly delivers a superior champagne
at this price level: bakery nose, lively fruit and mousse, a
sense of mellowness from unhurried maturation.

Nobody does it like Waitrose. At the tasting this summer, 110 of the wines they showed were entirely new. 'Our point of difference', says wine boss Pierpaolo Petrassi, 'is unparalleled choice and quality together with exceptional value for money'.

Yes, I know it sounds like the usual mantra in a business as ferociously competitive as supermarket retailing. But Pierpaolo has more than a point. With a choice of more than 1,000 wines, extending from a burgeoning everyday own-label range to the finest of fine wines and the best choice of fortifieds and stickies, Waitrose really is different.

In keeping with this principle, one highlight this year is the expanded choice of Australian wines. Although cheaper Aussie wines have been getting a bad press, it was those costing under £10 that impressed me most. This is a theme throughout. Waitrose might be tarnished as the poshest of the supermarkets, but the value given is beyond question; fewer than half of the 80-plus wines I have picked out here are priced above £10.

I cannot resist also mentioning some of the spectacular wines above the £10 mark, because Waitrose does offer a formidable choice. Hermitage Cave de Tain 2011 at £26.99 is one. Hermitage is the senior red wine of France's northern Rhône Valley and a proper rarity priced much higher than this from the handful of individual growers who make it. This one, from the local growers' co-operative, is a genuinely glorious example of the style and well worth saving up for. What other supermarket does this?

One more: Willi Haag Brauneberger Juffer-Sonnenuhr Riesling Auslese 2015 at £16.99 is a dawn-fresh new Moselle that tastes every bit as exotic as it sounds. It immeasurably deepens the mystery of German wine's unloved status in Britain but utterly fascinates in its own right.

OK, these classics are sold only in a few of Waitrose's giant stores. But you can get them, along with all the rest of the range, online, by the single bottle. What other supermarket does this?'

Waitrose are forever redesigning and reconfiguring their stores, especially the wine sections, which I wish they wouldn't, but at least they are consistent about offering discounts. Every month they knock up to a third off countless excellent wines, and for that, Waitrose, thank you very much.

RED WINES

 **8 Norton Winemaker's Reserve
Malbec 2013** £11.99

Friendly monster from venerable English-founded winery is richly ripe with hallmark Mendoza Malbec darkness and sinew but finely balanced besides; 14.5% alcohol.

8 Storm Tree Shiraz 2015 £5.79

I had thought drinkable Aussie wine at this price extinct but this party red, plump but vigorous and full of eager bounce (and 14.5% alcohol) suggests otherwise.

**9 Parker Favourite Son Cabernet
Sauvignon 2014** £7.49

Dark and tannic but friendly and balanced juicy-blackcurranty Coonawarra wine has a light touch along with its oaked sleekness and evident ripeness (14.5% alcohol); it's made by Phil Lehmann, son of late legendary winemaker Peter Lehmann; it bodes well and it's good value.

**9 James Irvine Signature Selection
Merlot 2014** £7.99

James Irvine, lately retired as Australia's king of Merlot, is handsomely saluted in this lush and instantly likeable choc 'n' cherry food (duck, please) red of well-judged intensity and taut finish with 14.8% alcohol. It's from the Red Dirt vineyard at Wrattonbully in the Barossa, made by Joanne Irving, James's redoubtable daughter.

RED WINES

AUSTRALIA

♟ 8 De Bortoli Daydream Pinot Noir 2015 £9.79
Aussie Pinot is very distinct from Kiwi Pinot, as illustrated by this firmly ripe and generous, cherry-sweet Yarra Valley wine of briskness and balance.

♟ 9 Wirra Wirra Church Block 2013 £13.49
Industry-standard McLaren Vale blend of Cabernet Sauvignon with Shiraz and Merlot is as succulent and opulent as ever in its black-fruit lushness; 14.5% alcohol.

BRAZIL

♟ 8 Waitrose Brazilian Merlot 2013 £8.79
You might not guess this is Brazilian (who would?) but it's a likeable, natural-tasting, black-cherry-ripe easy-drinker made without oak, but with evident dedication.

FRANCE

♟ 8 Waitrose Southern French Grenache 2015 £6.49
Sweetly ripe (13.5% alcohol) and healthy outdoor Pays d'Oc with savoury spice and grip.

♟ 9 Corbières Saint Auriol 2015 £6.99
Crimson-dark Mediterranean winter warmer from an appellation that can suffer from harsh overripeness is on fine form with this friendly briary-spicy number in ideal balance; 13.5% alcohol.

♟ 8 Les Chartrons 2014 £7.99
Generic claret has vivid but developed ripe black fruits and a convincing Bordeaux balance; safe bet.

♟ 8 Château de Passedieu 2012 £8.99
From the Bordeaux hinterland of Côtes de Bourg, this is like a New World wine – deep crimson, sweetly aromatic (mostly Merlot) and plumply ripe (13.5% alcohol), but all in wholesome balance.

RED WINES

 8 **Les Dauphins Côtes du Rhône**
Villages 2015 £8.99

If you are attracted by the stylish retro label on this brand, be assured the wine lives up to it: vivid red-berry fruit with smooth depths and a warm spiciness auguring well for the 2015 vintage in the Rhône.

9 **Chinon Les Complices de Loire**
Les Graviers 2014 £9.99

Inky maroon colour to this glossy-plummy-greeny-fresh authentic Loire Cabernet Franc leads into big, ripe and gripping flavours; only in 18 mega-branches, or online.

9 **Réserve des Hospitaliers Cairanne 2014** £9.99

I've been following this Côtes du Rhône individual-village wine at Waitrose forever, enjoying its intense earthy-peppery-truffly and darkly tannic style. It's always been fair value (and frequently discounted) too, but from the 2015 Cairanne will be elevated to a 'cru' appellation along with Châteauneuf du Pape et al, and prices might be hiked. Buy this bold, distinctive bargain while you can; 13.5% alcohol.

8 **Morgon Domaine des Bassets 2015** £11.99

You're supposed to keep the wines of the Beaujolais cru Morgon a year or two before drinking, but this one is already gloriously evolved, juicy and bouncing with fleshy Gamay fruit; very ripe (14% alcohol) and stimulating.

8 **Domaine Paul Blanck Pinot Noir 2014** £14.99

Only Waitrose among the supermarkets does anything as esoteric as this, but Alsace Pinot is a discovery worth making: this one's fruit-packed, keen-edged and definitively Pinot; rare treat, at a price.

RED WINES

FRANCE

🍷 8 **Chorey-les-Beaune Joseph Drouhin 2013** £17.49
Silky and long-flavoured village Burgundy by safely reliable Drouhin evokes raspberries and cream in the best oaked Pinot Noir tradition; worth the price.

🍷 9 **Blason des Papes Châteauneuf du
Pape 2014** £20.99
A strikingly good Châteauneuf in spite of its bland nomenclature and recent vintage, this is slinky, blackly spicy and rounded with piquancy in the multi-layered fruits; 14% alcohol. It seems frequently on promo at one third off: £13.99.

🍷 8 **Château Cantin 2012** £23.99
A blood-red and rather regal St Emilion Grand Cru shining with rich cassis fruit and creamy from new oak contact, already drinking very well; handy last-minute buy for a special occasion; 13.5% alcohol.

🍷 9 **Hermitage Cave de Tain 2011** £26.99
Hermitage is one of France's greatest, rarest and costliest wines, and this one is the genuine article, pure Syrah from the Hermitage hill that rises steeply up from the Rhône river, a big, dense wine, earthy-gamey in its savour, long and silky and gripping; drinking well now, it will surely develop for years; price is perfectly fair and I've seen it on promo down to £19.99 – a steal.

ITALY

🍷 8 **Villa Pani Vino Rosso** £5.99
Made largely from Sangiovese, the grape of Chianti, this Romagna-Abruzzo party red has a pleasing lift of red fruit, a suggestion of almondy ripeness and a clean lipsmacking finish.

RED WINES

ITALY

🍷 8 **Recchia Bardolino 2015**   £7.99
Delicate but perky and well-knit cherry-fruit wine from
once-fashionable Verona appellation is of more than
mere nostalgic interest: a distinctive dry red to enjoy cool.

🍷 8 **Araldica Corsini Barbaresco 2013**   £11.99
Piedmont perennial in another good vintage, already
drinking well – limpid colour, sweet intense black cherry
perfume and plump but defined slinky fruit; 14% alcohol.

PORTUGAL

🍷 9 **Lisboa Bonavita 2014**   £7.99
Every inch a Portuguese wine from native grapes, you
get dark, yielding blackcurranty fruit with mint and
eucalyptus in a smooth texture nicely wrapped up in a
firm tannic structure; it grows on you; 14.25% alcohol.

S. AFRICA

🍷 8 **Secret Cellar Shiraz/Grenache 2015**   £7.79
Well-made focused minty-spicy-silky steak-and-chips red
has the keynote poise of ripe but carefully judged Cape
reds; wholesome and impressive; 13.7% alcohol.

SPAIN

🍷 8 **Valle de Viento Old Vines Cariñena 2013**   £6.49
From Cariñena grapes grown in the northwestern region
of Cariñena, a long-aged (2016 bottled) sweet plummy-
mulberry food red of distinctly likeable style, nicely
balanced.

🍷 8 **Waitrose Rioja Vega Ariana 2014**   £6.75
Quite pale to look at, but a nicely built crianza with a
white pepper highlight in the firm black fruit; a simple
typical Rioja with good ripeness and 14% alcohol.

RED WINES

SPAIN

🍷 9 **Scala Dei Prior 2013**   £7.99

Scala Dei (God's ladder) is the oldest winery in Catalonia's renowned Priorat wine region, named from the priory founded by Carthusians in 1162 at the place a local shepherd had a vision of angels rising up a stairway to heaven. It's an uplifting story and the same goes for the wine – huge, complex, velvety and 15% alcohol. The price seems modest but the wine is only in London mega-branches or online at Waitrose Cellar. Do try it.

🍷 10 **The Cubist Old Vine Calatayud**
Garnacha 2014   £9.99

Closely concentrated dark-hearted Zaragoza red has been a Waitrose regular for many years, lately rebranded with the Cubist tag, presumably in tribute to Picasso (from Catalonia rather than Calatayud, but never mind), and now comes up with the best vintage I can remember. Made without oak, it's nevertheless gorgeously lush and spicy with intense cassis-bramble fruit and theatrical heft and grip; 14.5% alcohol.

🍷 9 **Baron de Ley Rioja Reserva 2011**   £12.49

Unusually dark, dense and muscular, this is still very much in the grand Rioja style, creamily oaked and long on juicy blackcurrant fruit; still in its youth, I suppose, but already a delight to drink; 13.5% alcohol.

USA

🍷 8 **Fog Head Reserve Pinot Noir 2013**   £14.99

The name references the misty climate conditions in the Monterey, California vineyard rather than the morning-after effects: instantly likeable raspberry-nosed, delicate but engagingly intense sunny Pinot of lush savour; 13.5% alcohol.

RED WINES

SPAIN

🍷 8 **Frog's Leap Zinfandel 2013**   £24.99

Famous Napa Valley estate demonstrates what California's signature grape can do: a dark, luscious minty-blackberry wine with toasty aromas and elegantly trimmed balance, very ripe but very poised, too; an experience; 13.8% alcohol. Mega-stores and online.

PINK WINES

FRANCE

🍷 8 **Champteloup Rosé d'Anjou 2015**   £7.99

Loire pink has glowing magenta colour, orchard blossom nose with plenty of fresh fruit salad variety in the flavours; I'd dare to call it a commercial pink, fresh but with ingratiating sweetness; 10.75% alcohol.

🍷 8 **Le Bijou de Sophie Valrose Rosé 2015**   £8.49

Sophie Valrose's jewel of a rosé from Waitrose – I think we get the message. From the Languedoc appellation of Cabrières, it's a Cinsault-Grenache blend giving pale salmon colour, a crisp strawberry perfume and soft matching fresh fruitiness with clean citrus acidity and a ripe 13.5% alcohol.

🍷 8 **Thierry Delaunay Le Grand Ballon**
    Rosé 2015   £8.49

Mainly Gamay (as in red Beaujolais) from the Loire, it has a smoked-salmon hue, tangy summer-soft-fruit nose and corresponding lively fruit finishing cleanly dry – and nothing like Beaujolais.

🍷 8 **Mirabeau Pure Rosé 2015**   £12.99

I believe you have to like rosé a lot to pay this sort of price, but this very pale and dry Côte de Provence certainly impresses with its nettly freshness, nuanced summer-fruit flavours and lingering complex lushness.

WHITE WINES

Waitrose (vertical side text)

ARGENTINA

🍷 **8** **Riverglen View Chardonnay 2015** £5.99
Straight ripe-peachy clean-edged party Chardy at a keen price.

🍷 **9** **Catena Chardonnay 2015** £12.99
Waitrose has other, cheaper Argentine chardonnays, but save up for this one: world-class, richly coloured, lushly ripe and long-matured (some new oak) wine of generosity and elegant weight; 13.5% alcohol.

AUSTRALIA

🍷 **8** **Fox Gordon 'Sassy' Sauvignon Blanc 2015** £7.99
Sassy is the nickname of Sarah Atkins, a young member of the family owners of Fox Gordon. I suppose this asparagus-evoking, lively and expressive Adelaide Hills wine could almost be thus described; very friendly and uplifting and good value.

🍷 **8** **De Bortoli Daydream Chardonnay 2015** £9.79
Immediately likeable mineral-but-luscious Yarra Valley dry wine by dependable but whimsically inclined De Bortoli hails from vineyards with names including Tarrawarra and Woori Yallock. Who could possibly resist?

AUSTRIA

🍷 **9** **Waitrose Grüner Veltliner 2015** £7.99
There's a hint of green in the colour and the distinct pleasantly musky aroma that are hallmarks of Austria's national grape in this exotic dry wine, a fine match for assertive, spicy dishes; good example fairly priced.

WHITE WINES

8 Muscadet La Marinière 2015 £5.99
Attractively presented easy-to-like Loire classic has
briskly refreshing quality: tangy rather than green and
sharp as humbler Muscadets can be; 11.5% alcohol.

**9 Fief Guérin Muscadet sur Lie Côtes
de Grandlieu 2015** £7.99
My favourite Muscadet comes not from the famed
vineyards adjacent to the rivers Sèvre and Maine east of
Nantes but out of the little enclave of Grandlieu south
of the city. In this vintage you get a lovely brisk and
briny white-fruit aroma and lashings of leesy, joined-up
corresponding flavours; no greenness, more a decisive,
lemon-twangy freshness making a brilliant shellfish
match; 11.79% alcohol, it says here.

8 Hen-Pecked Picpoul de Pinet 2015 £7.99
Crisply fresh and tangy rendering of fashionable Picpoul
complete with tee-hee brand name is better than the
gimmickry might suggest. Curiously, only in 63 of the
350-plus stores.

8 Côté Mas Vermentino 2015 £8.49
Pays d'Oc dry (very dry) wine from go-to variety
Vermentino by ubiquitous regional winemaker Jean
Claude Mas makes an aromatic, fleetingly minty orchard-
fruit refresher of uncommon interest.

**9 Mâcon-Villages Cave de Lugny
Chardonnay 2015** £8.79
Cave de Lugny in Burgundy's Mâconnais supplies lots
of UK outlets, but this wine is reportedly exclusive to
Waitrose. It's worth the journey: sunnily ripe but super-
fresh white-peach and lush dry wine of lovely balance and
weight; 13.5% alcohol.

FRANCE

WHITE WINES

9 Domaine des Forges Coteaux du Layon
Premier Cru Chaume 2014 37.5cl £8.99

You need to be predisposed towards sweet wines to take an interest in this rarity from the Loire Valley. It's a pure-gold late-harvest Chenin Blanc at its glorious richest, demonstrating perfectly the grape's magical ability to balance nectar and citrus in true harmony. An experience and not expensive for what it is; 11.5% alcohol.

8 Champteloup Sauvignon Blanc 2015 £8.99

Generic Touraine dry refresher has a good spike of emerald zing on the nose and long grassy flavours with lushness all the way; an 'everyday' Loire wine of a quality well above routine.

8 Laurent Miquel Vendanges Nocturnes
Viognier 2015 £8.99

The idea of harvesting grapes at night is that the picked fruit is not exposed to the blazing sun and the risk of spontaneous fermentation, as well it might where this wine is made in the Languedoc. Result is a dry, pleasingly ascetic Viognier of bright freshness, but still with the candied apricot richness that is the grape's keynote.

9 Domaine Begude Terroir 11300
Chardonnay 2015 £9.99

The number here is the postcode of Limoux in the Aude, whence cometh this emphatic Chardonnay of peachy lushness (some oak) and interesting chalky minerality, all very elegantly poised and somehow more than the sum of its parts; 13.45% alcohol.

WHITE WINES

8 Cave de Turckheim Alsace
Gewürztraminer 2015 £9.99

The Turckheim co-op's monopoly of Gewürz supplies to UK supermarkets is fascinating, but I believe the wines do vary occasionally between outlets. This new vintage has a potent lychee perfume, soft, exotic tropical-spicy classic fruit and a tang of citrus acidity that tops out the sweetness nicely.

8 Seriously Peachy from Waitrose
Pacherenc du Vic Bilh 2013 37.5cl £9.99

Gorgeous pale-gold sweet aperitif/dessert Gascon wine in the Sauternes style but at a fraction of Sauternes price; honeyed and, indeed, peachy, but with a lifting fruit freshness.

8 Le Gardien de Saint Pierre
Chardonnay 2015 £10.99

Leesy unoaked Mâcon gives off what I like to call a buttery scrambled egg aroma that gives on to a fine sweet-apple fruit with spearmint suggestions completed with a delicate lemon acidity; in short, a nice dry white wine.

8 Waitrose Chablis 2015 £11.99

My note on this is unhelpfully trite. 'Yes, very good of its kind', it says. 'Natural and in the true Chablis style'.

8 Pouilly-Fuissé Marc Dudet 2013 £15.99

Top-drawer Mâconnais has a fine fruit-salad nose with a lemon twang; in the mouth it's deliciously peachy and mineral, enriched not by oak contact but time on the lees – a wholesomely natural process that translates into the purity of style.

WHITE WINES

FRANCE

🍷 8 **Chevalier-Montrachet Grand Cru**
Les Demoiselles Louis Latour 2013 £185.00
It's very kind of Waitrose – or more likely Louis Latour – to share this sort of wine with scribblers like me, so here's my report: It's pure gold. If I could genuinely afford a lavish, new-oak-matured, plush and perfectly pitched white Burgundy like this I would drink it all the time; 14% alcohol. In 9 megastores or online.

🍷 8 **Waitrose German Dry Riesling 2015** £7.99
Zippy, racy, appley-lemony fermented-out Moselle is as dry as the label avers, and simply delicious. A new addition, I believe, to Waitrose's compact own-label wine range.

GERMANY

🍷 9 **Willi Haag Brauneberger Juffer-Sonnenuhr**
Riesling Auslese 2015 £16.99
On tasting day, Waitrose put this among its 'Sweet Wines' but it is in fact a racy, gloriously grapy-ripe Moselle in which the ambrosial richness is incidental to the thrill of the Riesling rush; fabulous auslese at a forgivable price with just 7.5% alcohol. Sadly, only in 6 megastores but also online.

HUNGARY

🍷 8 **Hilltop Estate Pinot Grigio 2015** £6.99
Decent effort from the Neszmély region, northwest of Budapest, has crisp white fruit with an extra ripeness perhaps contributed by the 15% Chardonnay in the mix.

WHITE WINES

9 Waitrose Gavi La Rotonda 2015   £7.49
Gavi, Piedmont's cool dry white from Cortese grapes, is
now everywhere, but not universally interesting. This one
shines: fresh and lush with a balance between white stone
fruit and blanched-nut creaminess, completed with a neat
citrus edge; it makes a real impression.

8 Pecorino Terre di Cheti 2015   £7.99
Sheep on the label are always a draw, here denoting that
Cheti in the Abruzzo, source of this wine, is a major
sheep-farming area. Nice wine, too, from the Pecorino
grape – so named after pecora, Italian for sheep – which
also flourishes in Cheti: it's apple/pear fresh and dry with
a little almondy creaminess.

**8 Forte Alto Pinot Grigio Vigneti delle
Dolomiti 2015**   £8.99
Italian PG always seems to me very much the better for
coming from the sub-Alpine regions of Trentino, as this
one does, rather than the plains of the Veneto to the
south. Here you get crispness and suggestions of smoky
pungency amid the orchard fruit.

9 Tre Fiori Greco di Tufo 2015   £10.99
Greco grapes, so known because Greeks imported them
into Italy 3,000 years back, grown in the Tufo commune
of the Campania here produce a complex wine with lots
of colour, a basketful of fruits and herbs evoked in the
aroma and flavour and a twangy citrus finish; seriously
versatile food matcher.

WHITE WINES

ITALY

🍷 8 **Crociani Vin Santo di Montepulciano 2011 37.5cl** £19.49

Tuscan speciality wine made from grapes dried out for months to concentrate the juice (8lb of new-picked fruit per half bottle) is bronze and sherry-like with a unique marzipan sweetness; gorgeous and 16% alcohol.

NEW ZEALAND

🍷 8 **The Ned Pinot Grigio 2015** £9.45

Brilliantly named dry Marlborough wine (The Ned is a peak of the Waihopai Valley) is the only PG I know allowed to extract some of the grape's pink skin colour, and very fetching it looks. Lovely pungent, smoky savour to the perky, super-fresh flavour; 13.5% alcohol. It seems perpetually on price promo so is a frequent bargain.

🍷 8 **Hartley's Block Sauvignon Blanc 2015** £10.39

Jump-out nettly-grassy Waihopai (Marlborough) wine is almost severe in its dry impact, but the fruit runs deep and long.

🍷 8 **Waitrose Marlborough Sauvignon Blanc 2015** £10.49

Made for Waitrose by estimable Villa Maria, a very bright and grassy-lush crowd-pleaser with sweetly ripe flavours in cunning balance to the crunchy citrus zest.

🍷 8 **Greystone Sauvignon Blanc 2015** £14.99

Sweetly oaked creaminess in this tangy Waipara wine is an artful confection, with freshness neatly retained; nice buy for those who like this sort of thing; 13.5% alcohol.

WHITE WINES

S. AFRICA

🍷 **8** **Morgenhof Estate Chenin Blanc 2015** £11.99

Lusciousness and lime are in ideal counterpoint in this artfully oaked Stellenbosch dry wine, a fine illustration of the Chenin Blanc's delightful powers of balance; 13.5% alcohol.

🍷 **9** **Waitrose Aromatic and Citrus**
      Spanish Dry White £4.99

Anonymous non-vintage budget wine accords precisely with the description and is a joy. The grapes, mostly humble Airen with Verdejo and Sauvignon Blanc, are grown 'on acidic, sandy soils with typical Mediterranean climate with Atlantic influences'.

SPAIN

🍷 **8** **Waitrose Libra Verdejo 2015** £7.49

Dry, bright wine has the clean freshness and vegetal-grassy-nutty Verdejo flavours that are the hallmark of the (relatively) cool-climate region of Rueda in Spain's northwest.

🍷 **8** **Waitrose Viña Taboexa Albariño 2015** £7.99

Distinctive northwest-coast refresher owes some of its bracing freshness to the Atlantic mists that allow for a long ripening process that retains acidity in the wine; delicious with everything fishy.

USA

🍷 **8** **Bonterra Organic Chardonnay 2014** £11.99

Long-serving Californian brand seems to me back on form after a bit of a pause; it's partly oak-matured and this shows up plainly in the toffee-apple aroma, but there's a nice rush of crisp-apple fruit and lemony twang bringing it all into a convincing natural balance; 13.5% alcohol. Frequently discounted.

FORTIFIED WINES

PORTUGAL

Waitrose

9 Quinta do Noval 10-Year-Old Tawny Port £24.99
By a comfortable margin the most delicious of all the
10-year-old tawnies I have tasted through the year, this
is seductively glossy, figgy-raisiny-rich with marzipan
mintiness and a lovely lift of acidity. It's expensive but
worth it, and look out for occasional useful discounts;
19.6% alcohol.

8 Williams & Humbert Alegria Manzanilla
Sherry 37.5cl £5.29
Disorientingly packaged as if it were beer, this thrillingly
briny-tangy bone-dry pale sherry is cracklingly fresh and
stimulating and good value besides; 15% alcohol. Drink
ice cold, just like beer.

9 Waitrose Solera Jerezano Fino del
Puerto Sherry £9.99
Very pale, pungent and alive with smoky savour, a
memorably fresh and tinglingly dry fino of great character
made by Lustau for Waitrose's brilliant Solera Jerezano
range – all in the same quality league as this one; 16.5%
alcohol.

SPAIN

9 Bodegas Cayetano del Pino Y Cia
Palo Cortado Solera Sherry 37.5cl £11.49
Beautifully presented little half bottle brings you a rare
amber sherry jiggling with fruits and nuts amid an almost
spiritous silkiness; very old sherry but bright, vivid and
stimulating too; aficionados should not miss out on this;
20% alcohol. In 38 megastores only but online as well.

FORTIFIED WINES

SPAIN

 **9 Williams & Humbert 'As You Like It'
Amontillado Sherry 37.5cl**   £22.99
Lured by the ludicrous name and outrageous price, I had
to try this 'precious relic' (to quote Waitrose) and found a
ravishing, copper-gold, honeyed but essentially naturally
dry amontillado that will have sherry aficionados in
raptures. A rare treat beyond delineation with 20.5%
alcohol.

SPARKLING WINES

ENGLAND

8 Leckford Estate Brut 2012   £29.99
From the same grape varieties that go into champagne,
but here grown at a Waitrose-owned farm in Hampshire,
a very dry single-harvest sparkler of brisk, lemony
liveliness; nothing like champagne but a pleasure to drink
just the same.

8 Black Dog Hill Classic Cuvée 2011   £30.00
Credit must go to Waitrose for selling so many English
fizzes – seven were on offer on the day I tasted – even
though most are available only online, as this Sussex
sparkler is. It's from the champagne formula of
Chardonnay, Pinot Noir and Pinot Meunier, excitingly
fruity and piquant, even peppery in its freshness and
zeal. Not like champagne, but a real treat for patriotic
celebrants.

SPARKLING WINES

9 Cave de Lugny Sparkling Burgundy
Blanc de Blancs £13.49

The description Sparkling Burgundy seems a prosaic substitute for the 'Crémant de Bourgogne' of old but the appeal of this perennial pure Chardonnay remains as effervescently irresistible as ever. It's a cracking creamy ever-so-champagne-like non-vintage fizz of evident maturity and roundness with lemony tang and yeasty richness. Often on discount at around a tenner, it's affectionately known in the Halley household as Cuvée Alison.

8 Champagne Bredon Cuvée
Jean Louis Brut £22.99

Comforting bready-yeasty Pinot Noir-led wine feels smoothly assured and delivers mellow fruit that speaks of long bottle-age; very nice contrivance, especially at the frequent promo price of £14.99.

8 Waitrose Blanc de Blancs
Champagne Brut £22.99

All-Chardonnay in-house perennial is made from fruit harvested in 2012, but its mellow nature suggests greater age; detectable Chardonnay character with creaminess of mousse and ripe fruit.

10 Waitrose Brut Special Réserve
Vintage 2005 £24.99

My champagne of the year. It's been in the bottle a decade and delivers a correspondingly mellow colour, buttered-toast aromas and rich but crisply defined fruit; unmistakably brilliant champagne from a celebrated vintage at a price that seems pitched needlessly low.

SPARKLING WINES

8 **Louis Roederer Cristal Champagne 2007 £150.00**

FRANCE

So what does the footballers' favourite fizz taste like? Thank you, Waitrose, who sell this in no fewer than 181 of their stores, for the chance to find out. It has the gold colour of long ageing, echoes in the aroma of bakeries and marbled halls and while not bigger or richer than humbler rivals, it has an integrity of flavour that is ineffably reassuring.

7 **Calle d'Oro Prosecco** **£10.49**

ITALY

I am blindly prejudiced (prejudice by its nature is blind, mind you) against prosecco but quite liked this just-off-dry number, peary and foamy, but surely not worth the shelf price. Its regular promotion tag of £6.99 is much nearer the mark; 11% alcohol.

—Making the most of it—

There has always been a lot of nonsense talked about the correct ways to serve wine. Red wine, we are told, should be opened and allowed to 'breathe' before pouring. White wine should be chilled. Wine doesn't go with soup, tomatoes or chocolate. You know the sort of thing.

It would all be simply laughable except that these daft conventions do make so many potential wine lovers nervous about the simple ritual of opening a bottle and sharing it around. Here is a short and opinionated guide to the received wisdom.

Breathing

Simply uncorking a wine for an hour or two before you serve it will make absolutely no difference to the way it tastes. However, if you wish to warm up an icy bottle of red by placing it near (never on) a radiator or fire, do remove the cork first. As the wine warms, even very slightly, it gives off gas, which will spoil the flavour if it cannot escape.

Chambré-ing

One of the more florid terms in the wine vocabulary. The idea is that red wine should be at the same temperature as the room (chambre) you're going to drink it in. In fairness, it makes sense – although the term harks back to the days when the only people who drank wine were those who could afford to keep it in the freezing cold vaulted cellars beneath their houses. The ridiculously high temperatures to which some homes are raised by central heating systems today are really far too warm for wine. But presumably those who live in such circumstances do so out of choice, and will prefer their wine to be similarly overheated.

Chilling

Drink your white wine as cold as you like. It's certainly true that good whites are at their best at a cool rather than at an icy temperature, but cheap and characterless wines can be improved immeasurably if they are cold enough – the anaesthetising effect of the temperature removes all sense of taste. Pay no attention to notions that red wine should not be served cool. There are plenty of lightweight reds that will respond very well to an hour in the fridge.

Corked wine

Wine trade surveys reveal that far too many bottles are in no fit state to be sold. The villain is very often cited as the cork. Cut from the bark of cork-oak trees cultivated for the purpose in Portugal and Spain, these natural stoppers have done sterling service for 200 years, but now face a crisis of confidence among wine producers. A diseased or damaged cork can make the wine taste stale because air has penetrated, or musty-mushroomy due to TCA, an infection of the raw material. These faults in wine, known as 'corked' or 'corky', should be immediately obvious, even in the humblest bottle, so you should return the bottle to the supplier and demand a refund.

Today, more and more wine producers are opting to close their bottles with polymer bungs. Some are designed to resemble the 'real thing' while others come in a rather disorienting range of colours – including black. While these things can be a pain to extract, there seems to be no evidence they do any harm to the wine. Don't 'lay down' bottles closed with polymer. The potential effects of years of contact with the plastic are yet to be scientifically established.

The same goes for screwcaps. These do have the merit of obviating the struggle with the corkscrew, but prolonged contact of the plastic liner with the wine might not be a good idea.

Corkscrews

The best kind of corkscrew is the 'waiter's friend' type. It looks like a pen-knife, unfolding a 'worm' (the helix or screw) and a lever device which, after the worm has been driven into the cork (try to centre it) rests on the lip of the bottle and enables you to withdraw the cork with minimal effort. Some have two-stage lips to facilitate the task. These devices are cheaper and longer-lasting than any of the more elaborate types, and are equally effective at withdrawing polymer bungs – which can be hellishly difficult to unwind from Teflon-coated 'continuous' corkscrews like the Screwpull.

Decanting

There are two views on the merits of decanting wines. The prevailing one seems to be that it is pointless and even pretentious. The other is that it can make real improvements in the way a wine tastes and is definitely worth the trouble.

Scientists, not usually much exercised by the finer nuances of wine, will tell you that exposure to the air causes wine to 'oxidise' – take in oxygen molecules that will quite quickly initiate the process of turning wine into vinegar – and anyone who has tasted a 'morning-after' glass of wine will no doubt vouch for this.

But the fact that wine does oxidise is a genuine clue to the reality of the effects of exposure to air. Shut inside its bottle, a young wine is very much a live substance, jumping with natural, but mysterious, compounds that can cause all sorts of strange taste sensations. But by exposing the wine to air these effects are markedly reduced.

In wines that spend longer in the bottle, the influence of these factors diminishes, in a process called 'reduction'. In red wines, the hardness of tannin – the natural preservative imparted into wine from the grape skins – gradually reduces, just as the raw purple colour darkens to ruby and later to orangey-brown.

I believe there is less reason for decanting old wines than new, unless the old wine has thrown a deposit and needs carefully to be poured off it. And in some light-bodied wines, such as older Rioja, decanting is probably a bad idea because it can accelerate oxidation all too quickly.

As to actual experiments, I have carried out several of my own, with wines opened in advance or wines decanted compared to the same wines just opened and poured, and my own unscientific judgement is that big, young, alcoholic reds can certainly be improved by aeration.

Washing glasses

If your wine glasses are of any value to you, don't put them in the dishwasher. Over time, they'll craze from the heat of the water. And they will not emerge in the glitteringly pristine condition suggested by the pictures on some detergent packets. For genuinely perfect glasses that will stay that way, wash them in hot soapy water, rinse with clean, hot water and dry immediately with a glass cloth kept exclusively for this purpose. Sounds like fanaticism, but if you take your wine seriously, you'll see there is sense in it.

Keeping wine

How long can you keep an opened bottle of wine before it goes downhill? Not long. A re-corked bottle with just a glassful out of it should stay fresh until the day after, but if there is a lot of air inside the bottle, the wine will oxidise, turning progressively stale and sour. Wine 'saving' devices that allow you to withdraw the air from the bottle via a punctured, self-sealing rubber stopper are variably effective, but don't expect these to keep a wine fresh for more than a couple of re-openings. A crafty method of keeping a half-finished bottle is to decant it, via a funnel, into a clean half bottle and recork.

Storing wine

Supermarket labels always seem to advise that 'this wine should be consumed within one year of purchase'. I think this is a wheeze to persuade customers to drink it up quickly and come back for more. Many of the more robust red wines are likely to stay in good condition for much more than one year, and plenty will actually improve with age. On the other hand, it is a sensible axiom that inexpensive dry white wines are better the younger they are. If you do intend to store wines for longer than a few weeks, do pay heed to the conventional wisdom that bottles are best stored in low, stable temperatures, preferably in the dark. Bottles closed with conventional corks should be laid on their side lest the corks dry out for lack of contact with the wine. But one of the notable advantages of the new closures now proliferating is that if your wine comes with a polymer 'cork' or a screwcap, you can safely store it upright.

Wine and food

Wine is made to be drunk with food, but some wines go better with particular dishes than others. It is no coincidence that Italian wines, characterised by soft, cherry fruit and a clean, mouth-drying finish, go so well with the sticky delights of pasta.

But it's personal taste rather than national associations that should determine the choice of wine with food. And if you prefer a black-hearted Argentinian Malbec to a brambly Italian Barbera with your Bolognese, that's fine.

The conventions that have grown up around wine and food pairings do make some sense, just the same. I was thrilled to learn in the early days of my drinking career that sweet, dessert wines can go well with strong blue cheese. As I don't much like puddings, but love sweet wines, I was eager to test this match – and I'm here to tell you that it works very well indeed as the end-piece to a grand meal in which there is cheese as well as pud on offer.

Red wine and cheese are supposed to be a natural match, but I'm not so sure. Reds can taste awfully tinny with soft cheeses such as Brie and Camembert, and even worse with goat's cheese. A really extravagant, yellow Australian Chardonnay will make a better match. Hard cheeses such as Cheddar and the wonderful Old Amsterdam (top-of-the-market Gouda) are better with reds.

And then there's the delicate issue of fish. Red wine is supposed to be a no-no. This might well be true of grilled and wholly unadorned white fish, such as sole or a delicate dish of prawns, scallops or crab. But what about oven-roasted monkfish or a substantial winter-season fish pie? An edgy red will do very well indeed, and provide much comfort for those many among us who simply prefer to drink red wine with food, and white wine on its own.

It is very often the method by which dishes are prepared, rather than their core ingredients, that determines which wine will work best. To be didactic, I would always choose Beaujolais or summer-fruit-style reds such as those from Pinot Noir grapes to go with a simple roast chicken. But if the bird is cooked as coq au vin with a hefty wine sauce, I would plump for a much more assertive red.

Some sauces, it is alleged, will overwhelm all wines. Salsa and curry come to mind. I have carried out a number of experiments into this great issue of our time, in my capacity as consultant to a company that specialises in supplying wines to Asian restaurants. One discovery I have made is that forcefully fruity dry white wines with keen acidity can go very well indeed even with fairly incendiary dishes. Sauvignon Blanc with Madras? Give it a try!

I'm also convinced, however, that some red wines will stand up very well to a bit of heat. The marvellously robust reds of Argentina made from Malbec grapes are good partners to Mexican chilli-hot recipes and salsa dishes. The dry, tannic edge to these wines provides a good counterpoint to the inflammatory spices in the food.

Some foods are supposedly impossible to match with wine. Eggs and chocolate are among the prime offenders. And yet, legendary cook Elizabeth David's best-selling autobiography was entitled *An Omelette and a Glass of Wine*, and the affiliation between chocolates and champagne is an unbreakable one. Taste is, after all, that most personally governed of all senses. If your choice is a boiled egg washed down with a glass of claret, who is to dictate otherwise?

What wine
words mean

Wine labels are getting crowded. It's mostly thanks to the unending torrent of new regulation. Lately, for example, the European Union has decided that all wines sold within its borders must display a health warning: 'Contains Sulphites'. All wines are made with the aid of preparations containing sulphur to combat diseases in the vineyards and bacterial infections in the winery. You can't make wine without sulphur. Even 'organic' wines are made with it. But some people are sensitive to the traces of sulphur in some wines, so we must all be informed of the presence of this hazardous material.

That's the way it is. And it might not be long before some even sterner warnings will be added about another ingredient in wine. Alcohol is the new tobacco, as the regulators see it, and in the near future we can look forward to some stern admonishments about the effects of alcohol. In the meantime, the mandatory information on every label includes the quantity, alcoholic strength and country of origin, along with the name of the producer. The region will be specified, vaguely on wines from loosely regulated countries such as Australia, and precisely on wines from over-regulated countries such as France. Wines from 'classic' regions of Europe – Bordeaux, Chianti, Rioja and so on – are mostly labelled according to their location rather than their constituent grape varieties. If it says Sancerre, it's taken as read that you either know it's made with Sauvignon Blanc grapes, or don't care.

Wines from just about everywhere else make no such assumptions. If a New Zealand wine is made from Sauvignon Blanc grapes, you can be sure the label will say so. This does quite neatly represent the gulf between the two worlds of winemaking. In traditional European regions, it's the place, the vineyard, that mostly determines the character of the wines. The French call it *terroir*, to encapsulate not just the lie of the land and the soil conditions but the wild variations in the weather from year to year as well. The grapes are merely the medium through which the timeless mysteries of the deep earth are translated into the ineffable glories of the wine, adjusted annually according to the vagaries of climate, variable moods of the winemaker, and who knows what else.

In the less arcane vineyards of the New World, the grape is definitely king. In hot valleys such as the Barossa (South Australia) or the Maipo (Chile), climate is relatively predictable and the soil conditions are managed by irrigation. It's the fruit that counts, and the style of the wine is determined by the variety – soft, spicy Shiraz; peachy, yellow Chardonnay and so on.

The main purpose of this glossary is, consequently, to give short descriptions of the 'classic' wines, including the names of the grapes they are made from, and of the 70-odd distinct grape varieties that make most of the world's wines. As well as these very brief descriptions, I have included equally shortened summaries of the regions and appellations of the better-known wines, along with some of the local terms used to indicate style and alleged qualities.

Finally, I have tried to explain in simple and rational terms the peculiar words I use in trying to convey the characteristics of wines described. 'Delicious' might need no further qualification, but the likes of 'bouncy', 'green' and 'liquorous' probably do.

A

abboccato – Medium-dry white wine style. Italy, especially Orvieto.

AC – *See* Appellation d'Origine Contrôlée.

acidity – To be any good, every wine must have the right level of acidity. It gives wine the element of dryness or sharpness it needs to prevent cloying sweetness or dull wateriness. If there is too much acidity, wine tastes raw or acetic (vinegary). Winemakers strive to create balanced acidity – either by cleverly controlling the natural processes, or by adding sugar and acid to correct imbalances.

aftertaste – The flavour that lingers in the mouth after swallowing the wine.

Aglianico – Black grape variety of southern Italy. It has romantic associations. When the ancient Greeks first colonised Italy in the seventh century BC, it was with the prime purpose of planting it as a vineyard (the Greek name for Italy was *Oenotria* – land of cultivated vines). The name for the vines the Greeks brought with them was Ellenico (as in Hellas, Greece), from which Aglianico is the modern rendering. To return to the point, these ancient vines, especially in the arid volcanic landscapes of Basilicata and Cilento, produce excellent dark, earthy and highly distinctive wines. A name to look out for.

Agriculture biologique – On French wine labels, an indication that the wine has been made by organic methods.

Albariño – White grape variety of Spain that makes intriguingly perfumed fresh and spicy dry wines, especially in esteemed Rias Baixas region.

alcohol – The alcohol levels in wines are expressed in terms of alcohol by volume ('abv'), that is, the percentage of the volume of the wine that is common, or ethyl, alcohol. A typical wine at 12 per cent abv is thus 12 parts alcohol and, in effect, 88 parts fruit juice.

The question of how much alcohol we can drink without harming ourselves in the short or long term is an impossible one to answer, but there is more or less general agreement among scientists that small amounts of alcohol are good for us, even if the only evidence of this is actuarial – the fact that mortality statistics show teetotallers live significantly shorter lives than moderate drinkers. The Department of Health now declares there is no safe level of alcohol consumption, but continues to advise that drinkers should not exceed a weekly number of 'units' of alcohol. A unit is 10ml of pure alcohol, the quantity contained in about half a 175ml glass of wine with 12 per cent alcohol. From 1995, the advisory limit on weekly units was 28 for men and 21 for women. This was reduced in 2016 to 14 for men and women alike.

Alentejo – Wine region of southern Portugal (immediately north of the Algarve), with a fast-improving reputation, especially for sappy, keen reds from local grape varieties including Aragones, Castelão and Trincadeira.

Almansa – DO winemaking region of Spain inland from Alicante, making great-value red wines.

Alsace – France's easternmost wine-producing region lies between the Vosges Mountains and the River Rhine, with Germany beyond. These conditions make for the production of some of the world's most delicious and fascinating white wines, always sold under the name of their constituent grapes. Pinot Blanc is the most affordable – and is well worth looking out for. The 'noble' grape varieties of the region are Gewürztraminer, Muscat, Riesling and Pinot Gris and they are always made on a single-variety basis. The richest, most exotic wines are those from individual *grand cru* vineyards, which are named on the label. Some *vendange tardive* (late harvest) wines are made, but tend to be expensive. All the wines are sold in tall, slim green bottles known as flûtes that closely resemble those of the Mosel, and the names of producers and grape varieties are often German too, so it is widely assumed that Alsace wines are German in style, if not in nationality. But this is not the case in either particular. Alsace wines are dry and quite unique in character – and definitely French.

Amarone – Style of red wine made in Valpolicella, Italy. Specially selected grapes are held back from the harvest and stored for several months to dry them out. They are then pressed and fermented into a highly concentrated speciality dry wine. Amarone means 'bitter', describing the dry style of the flavour.

amontillado – *See* sherry.

aperitif – If a wine is thus described, I believe it will give more pleasure before a meal than with one. Crisp, low-alcohol German wines and other delicately flavoured whites (including many dry Italians) are examples.

Appellation d'Origine Contrôlée – Commonly abbreviated to AC or AOC, this is the system under which quality wines are defined in France. About a third of the country's vast annual output qualifies, and there are more than 400 distinct AC zones. The declaration of an AC on the label signifies that the wine meets standards concerning location of vineyards and wineries, grape varieties and limits on harvest per hectare, methods of cultivation and vinification, and alcohol content. Wines are inspected and tasted by state-appointed committees. The one major aspect of any given wine that an AC cannot guarantee is that you will like it – but it certainly improves the chances.

Appellation d'Origine Protégée (AOP) – Under European Union rule changes, the AOC system is gradually transforming into AOP. In effect, it will mean little more than the exchange of 'controlled' with 'protected' on labels. One quirk of the new rules is that makers of AOP wines will be able to name the constituent grape variety or varieties on their labels, if they so wish.

Apulia – Anglicised name for Puglia.

Aragones – Synonym in Portugal, especially in the Alentejo region, for the Tempranillo grape variety of Spain.

Ardèche – Region of southern France to the west of the Rhône valley, home to a good vin de pays zone known as the Coteaux de L'Ardèche. Lots of decent-value reds from Syrah grapes, and some, less interesting, dry whites.

Arneis – White grape variety of Piedmont, north-west Italy. Makes dry whites with a certain almondy richness at often-inflated prices.

Assyrtiko – White grape variety of Greece now commonly named on dry white wines, sometimes of great quality, from the mainland and islands.

Asti – Town and major winemaking centre in Piedmont, Italy. The sparkling (spumante) sweet wines made from Moscato grapes are inexpensive and often delicious. Typical alcohol level is a modest 5 to 7 per cent.

attack – In wine tasting, the first impression made by the wine in the mouth.

Auslese – German wine-quality designation. *See* QmP.

B

Baga – Black grape variety indigenous to Portugal. Makes famously concentrated, juicy reds that get their deep colour from the grape's particularly thick skins. Look out for this name, now quite frequently quoted as the varietal on Portuguese wine labels. Often very good value for money.

balance – A big word in the vocabulary of wine tasting. Respectable wine must get two key things right: lots of fruitiness from the sweet grape juice, and plenty of acidity so the sweetness is 'balanced' with the crispness familiar in good dry whites and the dryness that marks out good reds. Some wines are noticeably 'well balanced' in that they have memorable fruitiness and the clean, satisfying 'finish' (last flavour in the mouth) that ideal acidity imparts.

Barbera – Black grape variety originally of Piedmont in Italy. Most commonly seen as Barbera d'Asti, the vigorously fruity red wine made around Asti – once better known for sweet sparkling Asti Spumante. Barbera grapes are now being grown in South America, often producing a sleeker, smoother style than at home in Italy.

Bardolino – Once fashionable, light red wine DOC of Veneto, north-west Italy. Bardolino is made principally from Corvina Veronese grapes plus Rondinella, Molinara and Negrara. Best wines are supposed to be those labelled Bardolino Superiore, a DOCG created in 2002. This classification closely specifies the permissible grape varieties and sets the alcohol level at a minimum of 12 per cent.

Barossa Valley – Famed vineyard region north of Adelaide, Australia, produces hearty reds principally from Shiraz, Cabernet Sauvignon and Grenache grapes, plus plenty of lush white wine from Chardonnay. Also known for limey, long-lived, mineral dry whites from Riesling grapes.

barrique – Barrel in French. *En barrique* on a wine label signifies the wine has been matured in oak.

Beaujolais – Unique red wines from the southern reaches of Burgundy, France, are made from Gamay grapes. Beaujolais nouveau, now deeply unfashionable, provides a friendly introduction to the bouncy, red-fruit style of the wine, but for the authentic experience, go for Beaujolais Villages, from the region's better, northern vineyards. There are ten AC zones within this northern sector making wines under their own names. Known as the *crus*, these are Brouilly, Chénas, Chiroubles, Côte de Brouilly, Fleurie, Juliénas, Morgon, Moulin à Vent, Regnié and St Amour and produce most of the best wines of the region. Prices are higher than those for Beaujolais Villages, but by no means always justifiably so.

Beaumes de Venise – Village near Châteauneuf du Pape in France's Rhône valley, famous for sweet and alcoholic wine from Muscat grapes. Delicious, grapey wines. A small number of growers also make strong (sometimes rather tough) red wines under the village name.

Beaune – One of the two winemaking centres (the other is Nuits St Georges) at the heart of Burgundy in France. Three of the region's humbler appellations take the name of the town: Côtes de Beaune, Côtes de Beaune Villages and Hautes Côtes de Beaune. Wines made under these ACs are often, but by no means always, good value for money.

berry fruit – Some red wines deliver a burst of flavour in the mouth that corresponds to biting into a newly picked berry – strawberry, blackberry, etc. So a wine described as having berry fruit (by this writer, anyway) has freshness, liveliness and immediate appeal.

bianco – White wine, Italy.

Bical – White grape variety principally of Dão region of northern Portugal. Not usually identified on labels, because most of it goes into inexpensive sparkling wines. Can make still wines of very refreshing crispness.

biodynamics – A cultivation method taking the organic approach several steps further. Biodynamic winemakers plant and tend their vineyards according to a date and time calendar 'in harmony' with the movements of the planets. Some of France's best-known wine estates subscribe, and many more are going that way. It might all sound bonkers, but it's salutary to learn that biodynamics is based on principles first described by a very eminent man, the Austrian educationist Rudolph Steiner.

bite – In wine tasting, the impression on the palate of a wine with plenty of acidity and, often, tannin.

blanc – White wine, France.

blanc de blancs – White wine from white grapes, France. May seem to be stating the obvious, but some white wines (e.g. champagne) are made, partially or entirely, from black grapes.

blanc de noirs – White wine from black grapes, France. Usually sparkling (especially champagne) made from black Pinot Meunier and Pinot Noir grapes, with no Chardonnay or other white varieties.

blanco – White wine, Spain and Portugal.

Blauer Zweigelt – Black grape variety of Austria, making a large proportion of the country's red wines, some of excellent quality.

Bobal – Black grape variety mostly of south-eastern Spain. Thick skin is good for colour and juice contributes acidity to blends.

bodega – In Spain, a wine producer or wine shop.

Bonarda – Black grape variety of northern Italy. Now more widely planted in Argentina, where it makes rather elegant red wines, often representing great value.

botrytis – Full name, *botrytis cinerea*, is that of a beneficent fungus that can attack ripe grape bunches late in the season, shrivelling the berries to a gruesome-looking mess, which yields concentrated juice of prized sweetness. Cheerfully known as 'noble rot', this fungus is actively encouraged by winemakers in regions as diverse as Sauternes (in Bordeaux), Monbazillac (in Bergerac), the Rhine and Mosel valleys, Hungary's Tokaji region and South Australia to make ambrosial dessert wines.

bouncy – The feel in the mouth of a red wine with young, juicy fruitiness. Good Beaujolais is bouncy, as are many north-west-Italian wines from Barbera and Dolcetto grapes.

Bourgogne Grand Ordinaire – Former AC of Burgundy, France. *See* Coteaux Bourguignons.

Bourgueil – Appellation of Loire Valley, France. Long-lived red wines from Cabernet Franc grapes.

briary – In wine tasting, associated with the flavours of fruit from prickly bushes such as blackberries.

brûlé – Pleasant burnt-toffee taste or smell, as in crème brûlée.

brut – Driest style of sparkling wine. Originally French, for very dry champagnes specially developed for the British market, but now used for sparkling wines from all round the world.

Buzet – Little-seen AC of south-west France overshadowed by Bordeaux but producing some characterful ripe reds.

C

Cabardès – AC for red and rosé wines from area north of Carcassonne, Aude, France. Principally Cabernet Sauvignon and Merlot grapes.

Cabernet Franc – Black grape variety originally of France. It makes the light-bodied and keenly edged red wines of the Loire Valley – such as Chinon and Saumur. And it is much grown in Bordeaux, especially in the appellation of St Emilion. Also now planted in Argentina, Australia and North America. Wines, especially in the Loire, are characterised by a leafy, sappy style and bold fruitiness. Most are best enjoyed young.

Cabernet Sauvignon – Black (or, rather, blue) grape variety now grown in virtually every wine-producing nation. When perfectly ripened, the grapes are smaller than many other varieties and have particularly thick skins. This means that when pressed, Cabernet grapes have a high proportion of skin to juice – and that makes for wine with lots of colour and tannin. In Bordeaux, the grape's traditional home, the grandest Cabernet-based wines have always been known as *vins de garde* (wines to keep) because they take years, even decades, to evolve as the effect of all that skin extraction preserves the fruit all the way to magnificent maturity. But in today's impatient world, these grapes are exploited in modern winemaking techniques to produce the sublime flavours of mature Cabernet without having to hang around for lengthy periods awaiting maturation. While there's nothing like a fine, ten-year-old claret (and nothing quite as expensive), there are many excellent Cabernets from around the world that amply illustrate this grape's characteristics. Classic smells and flavours include blackcurrants, cedar wood, chocolate, tobacco – even violets.

Cahors – An AC of the Lot Valley in south-west France once famous for 'black wine'. This was a curious concoction of straightforward wine mixed with a soupy must, made by boiling up new-pressed juice to concentrate it (through evaporation) before fermentation. The myth is still perpetuated that Cahors wine continues to be made in this way, but production on this basis actually ceased 150 years ago. Cahors today is no stronger, or blacker, than the wines of neighbouring appellations.

Cairanne – Village of the appellation collectively known as the Côtes du Rhône in southern France. Cairanne is one of several villages entitled to put their name on the labels of wines made within their AC boundary, and the appearance of this name is quite reliably an indicator of a very good wine indeed.

Calatayud – DO (quality wine zone) near Zaragoza in the Aragon region of northern Spain where they're making some astonishingly good wines at bargain prices, mainly reds from Garnacha and Tempranillo grapes. These are the varieties that go into the polished and oaky wines of Rioja, but in Calatayud, the wines are dark, dense and decidedly different.

Cannonau – Black grape native to Sardinia by name, but in fact the same variety as the ubiquitous Grenache of France (and Garnacha of Spain).

cantina sociale – *See* co-op.

Carignan – Black grape variety of Mediterranean France. It is rarely identified on labels, but is a major constituent of wines from the southern Rhône and Languedoc-Roussillon regions. Known as Carignano in Italy and Cariñena in Spain.

Cariñena – A region of north-east Spain, south of Navarra, known for substantial reds, as well as the Spanish name for the Carignan grape (*qv*).

Carmenère – Black grape variety once widely grown in Bordeaux but abandoned due to cultivation problems. Lately revived in South America where it is producing fine wines, sometimes with echoes of Bordeaux.

cassis – As a tasting note, signifies a wine that has a noticeable blackcurrant-concentrate flavour or smell. Much associated with the Cabernet Sauvignon grape.

Castelao – Portuguese black grape variety. Same as Periquita.

Catarratto – White grape variety of Sicily. In skilled hands it can make anything from keen, green-fruit dry whites to lush, oaked super-ripe styles. Also used for Marsala.

cat's pee – In tasting notes, a mildly jocular reference to a certain style of Sauvignon Blanc wine.

cava – The sparkling wine of Spain. Most originates in Catalonia, but the Denominación de Origen (DO) guarantee of authenticity is open to producers in many regions of the country. Much cava is very reasonably priced even though it is made by the same method as champagne – second fermentation in bottle, known in Spain as the *método clásico*.

CdR – Côtes du Rhône.

Cépage – Grape variety, French. 'Cépage Merlot' on a label simply means the wine is made largely or exclusively from Merlot grapes.

Chablis – Northernmost AC of France's Burgundy region. Its dry white wines from Chardonnay grapes are known for their fresh and steely style, but the best wines also age very gracefully into complex classics.

Chambourcin – Sounds like a cream cheese but it's a relatively modern (1963) French hybrid black grape that makes some good non-appellation lightweight-but-concentrated reds in the Loire Valley and now some heftier versions in Australia.

Chardonnay – The world's most popular grape variety. Said to originate from the village of Chardonnay in the Mâconnais region of southern Burgundy, the vine is now planted in every wine-producing nation. Wines are commonly characterised by generous colour and sweet-apple smell, but styles range from lean and sharp to opulently rich. Australia started the craze for oaked Chardonnay, the gold-coloured, super-ripe, buttery 'upfront' wines that are a caricature of lavish and outrageously expensive burgundies such as Meursault and Puligny-Montrachet. Rich to the point of egginess, these Aussie pretenders are now giving way to a sleeker, more minerally style with much less oak presence – if any at all. California and Chile, New Zealand and South Africa are competing hard to imitate the Burgundian style, and Australia's success in doing so.

Châteauneuf du Pape – Famed appellation centred on a picturesque village of the southern Rhône valley in France where in the 1320s French Pope Clement V had a splendid new château built for himself as a country retreat amidst his vineyards. The red wines of the AC, which can be made from 13 different grape varieties but principally Grenache, Syrah and Mourvèdre, are regarded as the best of the southern Rhône and have become rather expensive – but they can be sensationally good. Expensive white wines are also made.

Chenin Blanc – White grape variety of the Loire Valley, France. Now also grown farther afield, especially in South Africa. Makes dry, soft white wines and also rich, sweet styles. Sadly, many low-cost Chenin wines are bland and uninteresting.

cherry – In wine tasting, either a pale red colour or, more commonly, a smell or flavour akin to the sun-warmed, bursting sweet ripeness of cherries. Many Italian wines, from lightweights such as Bardolino and Valpolicella to serious Chianti, have this character. 'Black cherry' as a description is often used of Merlot wines – meaning they are sweet but have a firmness of flavour associated with the thicker skins of black cherries.

Cinsault – Black grape variety of southern France, where it is invariably blended with others in wines of all qualities ranging from vin de pays to the pricy reds of Châteauneuf du Pape. Also much planted in South Africa. The effect in wine is to add keen aromas (sometimes compared with turpentine!) and softness to the blend. The name is often spelt Cinsaut.

Clape, La – A small *cru* (defined quality-vineyard area) within the Coteaux du Languedoc where the growers make some seriously delicious red wines, mainly from Carignan, Grenache and Syrah grapes. A name worth looking out for on labels from the region.

claret – The red wine of Bordeaux, France. It comes from Latin *clarus*, meaning 'clear', recalling a time when the red wines of the region were much lighter in colour than they are now.

clarete – On Spanish labels indicates a pale-coloured red wine. Tinto signifies a deeper hue.

classed growth – English translation of French *cru classé* describes a group of 60 individual wine estates in the Médoc district of Bordeaux, which in 1855 were granted this new status on the basis that their wines were the most expensive at that time. The classification was a promotional wheeze to attract attention to the Bordeaux stand at that year's Great Exhibition in Paris. Amazingly, all of the 60 wines concerned are still in production and most still occupy more or less their original places in the pecking order price-wise. The league was divided up into five divisions from *Premier Grand Cru Classé* (just four wines originally, with one promoted in 1971 – the only change ever made to the classification) to *Cinquième Grand Cru Classé*. Other regions of Bordeaux, notably Graves and St Emilion, have since imitated Médoc and introduced their own rankings of *cru classé* estates.

classic – An overused term in every respect – wine descriptions being no exception. In this book, the word is used to describe a very good wine of its type. So, a 'classic' Cabernet Sauvignon is one that is recognisably and admirably characteristic of that grape.

Classico – Under Italy's wine laws, this word appended to the name of a DOC zone has an important significance. The classico wines of the region can only be made from vineyards lying in the best-rated areas, and wines thus labelled (e.g. Chianti Classico, Soave Classico, Valpolicella Classico) can be reliably counted on to be a cut above the rest.

Colombard – White grape variety of southern France. Once employed almost entirely for making the wine that is distilled for armagnac and cognac brandies, but lately restored to varietal prominence in the Vin de Pays des Côtes de Gascogne where high-tech wineries turn it into a fresh and crisp, if unchallenging, dry wine at a budget price. But beware, cheap Colombard (especially from South Africa) can still be very dull.

Conca de Barbera – Winemaking region of Catalonia, Spain.

co-op – Very many of France's good-quality, inexpensive wines are made by co-operatives. These are wine-producing factories whose members, and joint-owners, are local *vignerons* (vine growers). Each year they sell their harvests to the co-op for turning into branded wines. In Italy, co-op wines can be identified by the words *Cantina Sociale* on the label and in Germany by the term *Winzergenossenschaft*.

Corbières – A name to look out for. It's an AC of France's Midi (deep south) and produces countless robust reds and a few interesting whites, often at bargain prices.

Cortese – White grape variety of Piedmont, Italy. At its best, makes amazingly delicious, keenly brisk and fascinating wines, including those of the Gavi DOCG. Worth seeking out.

Costières de Nîmes – Until 1989, this AC of southern France was known as the Costières de Gard. It forms a buffer between the southern Rhône and Languedoc-Roussillon regions, and makes wines from broadly the same range of grape varieties. It's a name to look out for, the best red wines being notable for their concentration of colour and fruit, with the earthy-spiciness of the better Rhône wines and a likeable liquorice note. A few good white wines, too, and even a decent rosé or two.

Côte – In French, it simply means a side, or slope, of a hill. The implication in wine terms is that the grapes come from a vineyard ideally situated for maximum sunlight, good drainage and the unique soil conditions prevailing on the hill in question. It's fair enough to claim that vines grown on slopes might get more sunlight than those grown on the flat, but there is no guarantee whatsoever that any wine labelled 'Côtes du' this or that is made from grapes grown on a hillside anyway. Côtes du Rhône wines are a case in point. Many 'Côtes' wines come from entirely level vineyards and it is worth remembering that many of the vineyards of Bordeaux, producing most of the world's priciest wines, are little short of prairie-flat. The quality factor is determined much more significantly by the weather and the talents of the winemaker.

Coteaux Bourguignons – Generic AC of Burgundy, France, since 2011 for red and rosé wines from Pinot Noir and Gamay grapes, and white wines from (principally) Chardonnay and Bourgogne Aligoté grapes. The AC replaces the former appellation Bourgogne Grand Ordinaire.

Côtes de Blaye – Appellation Contrôlée zone of Bordeaux on the right bank of the River Gironde, opposite the more prestigious Médoc zone of the left bank. Best-rated vineyards qualify for the AC Premières Côtes de Blaye. A couple of centuries ago, Blaye (pronounced 'bligh') was the grander of the two, and even today makes some wines that compete well for quality, and at a fraction of the price of wines from its more fashionable rival across the water.

Côtes de Bourg – AC neighbouring Côtes de Blaye, making red wines of fast-improving quality and value.

Côtes du Luberon – Appellation Contrôlée zone of Provence in south-east France. Wines, mostly red, are similar in style to Côtes du Rhône.

Côtes du Rhône – One of the biggest and best-known appellations of south-east France, covering an area roughly defined by the southern reaches of the valley of the River Rhône. Long notorious for cheap and execrable reds, the Côtes du Rhône AC has lately achieved remarkable improvements in quality at all points along the price scale. Lots of brilliant-value warm and spicy reds, principally from Grenache and Syrah grapes. There are also some white and rosé wines.

Côtes du Rhône Villages – Appellation within the larger Côtes du Rhône AC for wine of supposed superiority made in a number of zones associated with a long list of nominated individual villages.

Côtes du Roussillon – Huge appellation of south-west France known for strong, dark, peppery reds often offering very decent value.

Côtes du Roussillon Villages – Appellation for superior wines from a number of nominated locations within the larger Roussillon AC. Some of these village wines can be of exceptional quality and value.

crianza – Means 'nursery' in Spanish. On Rioja and Navarra wines, the designation signifies a wine that has been nursed through a maturing period of at least a year in oak casks and a further six months in bottle before being released for sale.

cru – A word that crops up with confusing regularity on French wine labels. It means 'the growing' or 'the making' of a wine and asserts that the wine concerned is from a specific vineyard. Under the Appellation Contrôlée rules, countless *crus* are classified in various hierarchical ranks. Hundreds of individual vineyards are described as *premier cru* or *grand cru* in the classic wine regions of Alsace, Bordeaux, Burgundy and Champagne. The common denominator is that the wine can be counted on to be enormously expensive. On humbler wines, the use of the word *cru* tends to be mere decoration.

cru classé – *See* classed growth.

cuve – A vat for wine. French.

cuvée – French for the wine in a *cuve*, or vat. The word is much used on labels to imply that the wine is from just one vat, and thus of unique, unblended character. *Première cuvée* is supposedly the best wine from a given pressing because it comes from the free-run juice of grapes crushed by their own weight before pressing begins. Subsequent *cuvées* will have been from harsher pressings, grinding the grape pulp to extract the last drop of juice.

D

Dão – Major wine-producing region of northern Portugal now turning out much more interesting reds than it used to – worth looking out for anything made by mega-producer Sogrape.

demi sec – 'Half-dry' style of French (and some other) wines. Beware. It can mean anything from off-dry to cloyingly sweet.

DO – Denominación de Origen, Spain's wine-regulating scheme, similar to France's AC, but older – the first DO region was Rioja, from 1926. DO wines are Spain's best, accounting for a third of the nation's annual production.

DOC – Stands for Denominazione di Origine Controllata, Italy's equivalent of France's AC. The wines are made according to the stipulations of each of the system's 300-plus denominated zones of origin, along with a further 73 zones, which enjoy the superior classification of DOCG (DOC with *e Garantita* – guaranteed – appended).

DOCa – *Denominación de Origen Calificada* is Spain's highest regional wine classification; currently only Priorat and Rioja qualify.

DOP – Denominazione di Origine Protetta is an alternative classification to DOC (*qv*) under EU directive in Italy, comparable to AOP (*qv*) in France, but not yet widely adopted.

Durif – Rare black grape variety mostly of California, where it is also known as Petite Sirah, with some plantings in Australia.

E

earthy – A tricky word in the wine vocabulary. In this book, its use is meant to be complimentary. It indicates that the wine somehow suggests the soil the grapes were grown in, even (perhaps a shade too poetically) the landscape in which the vineyards lie. The amazing-value red wines of the torrid, volcanic southernmost regions of Italy are often described as earthy. This is an association with the pleasantly 'scorched' back-flavour in wines made from the ultra-ripe harvests of this near-sub-tropical part of the world.

edge – A wine with edge is one with evident (although not excessive) acidity.

élevé – 'Brought up' in French. Much used on wine labels where the wine has been matured (brought up) in oak barrels, *élevé en fûts de chêne*, to give it extra dimensions.

Entre Deux Mers – Meaning 'between two seas', it's a region lying between the Dordogne and Garonne rivers of Bordeaux, now mainly known for dry white wines from Sauvignon and Semillon grapes.

Estremadura – Wine-producing region occupying Portugal's coastal area north of Lisbon. Lots of interesting wines from indigenous grape varieties, usually at bargain prices. If a label mentions Estremadura, it is a safe rule that there might be something good within.

Extremadura – Minor wine-producing region of western Spain abutting the frontier with Portugal's Alentejo region. Not to be confused with Estremadura of Portugal (above).

F

Falanghina – Revived ancient grape variety of southern Italy now making some superbly fresh and tangy white wines.

Faugères – AC of the Languedoc in south-west France. Source of many hearty, economic reds.

Feteasca – White grape variety widely grown in Romania. Name means 'maiden's grape' and the wine tends to be soft and slightly sweet.

Fiano – White grape variety of the Campania of southern Italy and Sicily, lately revived. It is said to have been cultivated by the ancient Romans for a wine called Apianum.

finish – The last flavour lingering in the mouth after wine has been swallowed.

fino – Pale and very dry style of sherry. You drink it thoroughly chilled – and you don't keep it any longer after opening than other dry white wines. Needs to be fresh to be at its best.

Fitou – AC of Languedoc, France. Red wines principally from Carignan, Grenache, Mourvèdre and Syrah grapes.

flabby – Fun word describing a wine that tastes dilute or watery, with insufficient acidity.

Frappato – Black grape variety of Sicily. Light red wines.

fruit – In tasting terms, the fruit is the greater part of the overall flavour of a wine. The wine is (or should be) after all, composed entirely of fruit.

G

Gamay – The black grape that makes all red Beaujolais and some ordinary burgundy. It is a pretty safe rule to avoid Gamay wines from any other region, but there are exceptions.

Garganega – White grape variety of the Veneto region of north-east Italy. Best known as the principal ingredient of Soave, but occasionally included in varietal blends and mentioned as such on labels. Correctly pronounced 'gar-GAN-iga'.

Garnacha – Spanish black grape variety synonymous with Grenache of France. It is blended with Tempranillo to make the red wines of Rioja and Navarra, and is now quite widely cultivated elsewhere in Spain to make grippingly fruity varietals.

garrigue – Arid land of France's deep south giving its name to a style of red wine that notionally evokes the herby, heated, peppery flavours associated with such a landscape. A tricky metaphor!

Gavi – DOCG for dry but rich white wine from Cortese grapes in Piedmont, north-west Italy. Trendy Gavi di Gavi wines tend to be enjoyably lush, but are rather expensive.

Gewürztraminer – One of the great grape varieties of Alsace, France. At their best, the wines are perfumed with lychees and are richly, spicily fruity, yet quite dry. Gewürztraminer from Alsace can be expensive, but the grape is also grown with some success in Germany, Italy, New Zealand and South America, at more approachable prices. Pronounced 'ge-VOORTS-traminner'.

Givry – AC for red and white wines in the Côte Chalonnaise sub-region of Burgundy. Source of some wonderfully natural-tasting reds that might be lighter than those of the more prestigious Côte d'Or to the north, but have great merits of their own. Relatively, the wines are often underpriced.

Glera – Alternative name for Prosecco grape of northern Italy.

Godello – White grape variety of Galicia, Spain.

Graciano – Black grape variety of Spain that is one of the minor constituents of Rioja. Better known in its own right in Australia where it can make dense, spicy, long-lived red wines.

green – I don't often use this in the pejorative. Green, to me, is a likeable degree of freshness, especially in Sauvignon Blanc wines.

Grecanico – White grape variety of southern Italy, especially Sicily. Aromatic, grassy dry white wines.

Greco – White grape variety of southern Italy believed to be of ancient Greek origin. Big-flavoured dry white wines.

Grenache – The mainstay of the wines of the southern Rhône Valley in France. Grenache is usually the greater part of the mix in Côtes du Rhône reds and is widely planted right across the neighbouring Languedoc-Roussillon region. It's a big-cropping variety that thrives even in the hottest climates and is really a blending grape – most commonly with Syrah, the noble variety of the northern Rhône. Few French wines are labelled with its name, but the grape has caught on in Australia in a big way and it is now becoming a familiar varietal, known for strong, dark liquorous reds. Grenache is the French name for what is originally a Spanish variety, Garnacha.

Grillo – White grape of Sicily said to be among the island's oldest indigenous varieties, pre-dating the arrival of the Greeks in 600 BC. Much used for fortified Marsala, it has lately been revived for interesting, aromatic dry table wines.

grip – In wine-tasting terminology, the sensation in the mouth produced by a wine that has a healthy quantity of tannin in it. A wine with grip is a good wine. A wine with too much tannin, or which is still too young (the tannin hasn't 'softened' with age) is not described as having grip, but as mouth-puckering – or simply undrinkable.

Grolleau – Black grape variety of the Loire Valley principally cultivated for Rosé d'Anjou.

Gros Plant – White grape variety of the Pays Nantais in France's Loire estuary; synonymous with the Folle Blanche grape of south-west France.

Grüner Veltliner – The 'national' white-wine grape of Austria. In the past it made mostly soft, German-style everyday wines, but now is behind some excellent dry styles, too.

H

halbtrocken – 'Half-dry' in Germany's wine vocabulary. A reassurance that the wine is not some ghastly sugared Liebfraumilch-style confection.

hard – In red wine, a flavour denoting excess tannin, probably due to immaturity.

Haut-Médoc – Extensive AOC of Bordeaux accounting for the greater part of the vineyard area to the north of the city of Bordeaux and west of the Gironde river. The Haut-Médoc incorporates the prestigious commune-AOCs of Listrac, Margaux, Moulis, Pauillac, St Estephe and St Julien.

hock – The wine of Germany's Rhine river valleys. Traditionally, but no longer consistently, it comes in brown bottles, as distinct from the wine of the Mosel river valleys – which comes in green ones.

I

Indicación Geográfica Protegida – Spain's country-wine quality designation covers 46 zones across the country. Wines made under the IGP can be labelled Vino de la Tierra.

Indication Géographique Protégée (IGP) – Introduced to France in 2010 under EU-wide wine-designation rules, IGP covers the wines previously known as vins de pays. Some wines are currently labelled IGP, but established vins de pays producers are redesignating slowly, if at all, and are not obliged to do so. Some will abbreviate, so, for example, Vin de Pays d'Oc shortens to Pays d'Oc.

Indicazione Geografica Tipica – Italian wine-quality designation, broadly equivalent to France's IGP. The label has to state the geographical location of the vineyard and will often (but not always) state the principal grape varieties from which the wine is made.

isinglass – A gelatinous material used in fining (clarifying) wine. It is derived from fish bladders and consequently is eschewed by makers of 'vegetarian' wines.

J

jammy – The 'sweetness' in dry red wines is supposed to evoke ripeness rather than sugariness. Sometimes, flavours include a sweetness reminiscent of jam. Usually a fault in the winemaking technique.

Jerez – Wine town of Andalucia, Spain, and home to sherry. The English word 'sherry' is a simple mispronunciation of Jerez.

joven – Young wine, Spanish. In regions such as Rioja, *vino joven* is a synonym for *sin crianza*, which means 'without ageing' in cask or bottle.

Jura – Wine region of eastern France incorporating four AOCs, Arbois, Château-Chalon, Côtes du Jura and L'Etoile. Known for still red, white and rosé wines and sparkling wines as well as exotic *vin de paille* and *vin jaune*.

Jurançon – Appellation for white wines from Courbu and Manseng grapes at Pau, south-west France.

K

Kabinett – Under Germany's bewildering wine-quality rules, this is a classification of a top-quality (QmP) wine. Expect a keen, dry, racy style. The name comes from the cabinet or cupboard in which winemakers traditionally kept their most treasured bottles.

Kekfrankos – Black grape variety of Hungary, particularly the Sopron region, which makes some of the country's more interesting red wines, characterised by colour and spiciness. Same variety as Austria's Blaufrankisch.

L

Ladoix – Unfashionable AC at northern edge of Côtes de Beaune makes some of Burgundy's true bargain reds. A name to look out for.

Lambrusco – The name is that of a black grape variety widely grown across northern Italy. True Lambrusco wine is red, dry and very slightly sparkling, but from the 1980s Britain was deluged with a strange, sweet manifestation of the style, which has done little to enhance the good name of the original. Good Lambrusco is delicious and fun, but in this country now very hard to find.

Languedoc-Roussillon – Wine guaranteed to have been produced in France. The source, now, of many great-value wines from countless ACs and vin de pays zones.

lees – The detritus of the winemaking process that collects in the bottom of the vat or cask. Wines left for extended periods on the lees can acquire extra dimensions of flavour, in particular a 'leesy' creaminess.

legs – The liquid residue left clinging to the sides of the glass after wine has been swirled. The persistence of the legs is an indicator of the weight of alcohol. Also known as 'tears'.

lieu dit – This is starting to appear on French wine labels. It translates as an 'agreed place' and is an area of vineyard defined as of particular character or merit, but not classified under wine law. Usually, the *lieu dit*'s name is stated, with the implication that the wine in question has special value.

liquorice – The pungent, slightly burnt flavours of this once-fashionable confection are detectable in some wines made from very ripe grapes, for example, the Malbec harvested in Argentina and several varieties grown in the very hot vineyards of southernmost Italy. A close synonym is 'tarry'. This characteristic is by no means a fault in red wine, unless very dominant, but it can make for a challenging flavour that might not appeal to all tastes.

liquorous – Wines of great weight and glyceriney texture (evidenced by the 'legs', or 'tears', which cling to the glass after the wine has been swirled) are always noteworthy. The connection with liquor is drawn in respect of the feel of the wine in the mouth, rather than with the higher alcoholic strength of spirits.

Lirac – Village and AOC of southern Rhône Valley, France. A near-neighbour of the esteemed appellation of Châteauneuf du Pape, Lirac makes red wine of comparable depth and complexity, at competitive prices.

Lugana – DOC of Lombardy, Italy, known for a dry white wine that is often of real distinction – rich, almondy stuff from the ubiquitous Trebbiano grape.

M

Macabeo – One of the main grapes used for cava, the sparkling wine of Spain. It is the same grape as Viura.

Mâcon – Town and collective appellation of southern Burgundy, France. Lightweight white wines from Chardonnay grapes and similarly light reds from Pinot Noir and some Gamay. The better ones, and the ones exported, have the AC Mâcon-Villages and there are individual village wines with their own ACs including Mâcon-Clessé, Mâcon-Viré and Mâcon-Lugny.

Malbec – Black grape variety grown on a small scale in Bordeaux, and the mainstay of the wines of Cahors in France's Dordogne region under the name Cot. Now much better known for producing big butch reds in Argentina.

manzanilla – Pale, very dry sherry of Sanlucar de Barrameda, a resort town on the Bay of Cadiz in Spain. Manzanilla is proud to be distinct from the pale, very dry fino sherry of the main producing town of Jerez de la Frontera an hour's drive inland. Drink it chilled and fresh – it goes downhill in an opened bottle after just a few days, even if kept (as it should be) in the fridge.

Margaret River – Vineyard region of Western Australia regarded as ideal for grape varieties including Cabernet Sauvignon. It has a relatively cool climate and a reputation for making sophisticated wines, both red and white.

Marlborough – Best-known vineyard region of New Zealand's South Island has a cool climate and a name for brisk but cerebral Sauvignon Blanc and Chardonnay wines.

Marsanne – White grape variety of the northern Rhône Valley and, increasingly, of the wider south of France. It's known for making well-coloured wines with heady aroma and fruit.

Mataro – Black grape variety of Australia. It's the same as the Mourvèdre of France and Monastrell of Spain.

Mazuelo – Spanish name for France's black grape variety Carignan.

McLaren Vale – Vineyard region south of Adelaide in south-east Australia. Known for blockbuster Shiraz (and Chardonnay) that can be of great balance and quality from winemakers who keep the ripeness under control.

meaty – Weighty, rich red wine style.

Mencia – Black grape variety of Galicia and north-west Spain. Light red wines.

Mendoza – The region to watch in Argentina. Lying to the east of the Andes mountains, just about opposite the best vineyards of Chile on the other side, Mendoza accounts for the bulk of Argentine wine production, with quality improving fast.

Merlot – One of the great black wine grapes of Bordeaux, and now grown all over the world. The name is said to derive from the French *merle*, meaning a blackbird. Characteristics of Merlot-based wines attract descriptions such as 'plummy' and 'plump' with black-cherry aroma. The grapes are larger than most, and thus have less skin in proportion to their flesh. This means the resulting wines have less tannin than wines from smaller-berry varieties such as Cabernet Sauvignon, and are therefore, in the Bordeaux context at least, more suitable for drinking while still relatively young.

middle palate – In wine tasting, the impression given by the wine when it is held in the mouth.

Midi – Catch-all term for the deep south of France west of the Rhône Valley.

mineral – I am trying to excise this overused word from my notes, but not so far managing to do so with much conviction. To me it evokes flavours such as the stone-pure freshness of some Loire dry whites, or the steely quality of the more austere style of the Chardonnay grape, especially in Chablis. Mineral really just means something mined, as in dug out of the ground, like iron ore (as in steel) or rock, as in, er, stone. Maybe there's something in it, but I am not entirely confident.

Minervois – AC for (mostly) red wines from vineyards around the town of Minerve in the Languedoc-Roussillon region of France. Often good value. The new Minervois La Livinière AC – a sort of Minervois *grand cru* – is host to some great estates including Château Maris and Vignobles Lorgeril.

Monastrell – Black grape variety of Spain, widely planted in Mediterranean regions for inexpensive wines notable for their high alcohol and toughness – though they can mature into excellent, soft reds. The variety is known in France as Mourvèdre and in Australia as Mataro.

Monbazillac – AC for sweet, dessert wines within the wider appellation of Bergerac in south-west France. Made from the same grape varieties (principally Sauvignon and Semillon) that go into the much costlier counterpart wines of Barsac and Sauternes near Bordeaux, these stickies from botrytis-affected, late-harvested grapes can be delicious and good value for money.

Montalcino – Hill town of Tuscany, Italy, and a DOCG for strong and very long-lived red wines from Brunello grapes. The wines are mostly very expensive. Rosso di Montalcino, a DOC for the humbler wines of the zone, is often a good buy.

Montepulciano – Black grape variety of Italy. Best known in Montepulciano d'Abruzzo, the juicy, purply-black and bramble-fruited red of the Abruzzi region midway down Italy's Adriatic side. Also the grape in the rightly popular hearty reds of Rosso Conero from around Ancona in the Marches. Not to be confused with the hill town of Montepulciano in Tuscany, famous for expensive Vino Nobile di Montepulciano wine.

morello – Lots of red wines have smells and flavours redolent of cherries. Morello cherries, among the darkest coloured and sweetest of all varieties and the preferred choice of cherry-brandy producers, have a distinct sweetness resembled by some wines made from Merlot grapes. A morello whiff or taste is generally very welcome.

Moscatel – Spanish Muscat.

Moscato – *See* Muscat.

Moselle – The wine of Germany's Mosel river valleys, collectively known for winemaking purposes as Mosel-Saar-Ruwer. The wine always comes in slim, green bottles, as distinct from the brown bottles traditionally, but no longer exclusively, employed for Rhine wines.

Mourvèdre – Widely planted black grape variety of southern France. It's an ingredient in many of the wines of Provence, the Rhône and Languedoc, including the ubiquitous Vin de Pays d'Oc. It's a hot-climate vine and the wine is usually blended with other varieties to give sweet aromas and 'backbone' to the mix. Known as Mataro in Australia and Monastrell in Spain.

Muscadet – One of France's most familiar everyday whites, made from a grape called the Melon or Melon de Bourgogne. It comes from vineyards at the estuarial end of the River Loire, and has a sea-breezy freshness about it. The better wines are reckoned to be those from the vineyards in the Sèvre et Maine region, and many are made *sur lie* – 'on the lees' – meaning that the wine is left in contact with the yeasty deposit of its fermentation until just before bottling, in an endeavour to add interest to what can sometimes be an acidic and fruitless style.

Muscat – Grape variety with origins in ancient Greece, and still grown widely among the Aegean islands for the production of sweet white wines. Muscats are the wines that taste more like grape juice than any other – but the high sugar levels ensure they are also among the most alcoholic of wines, too. Known as Moscato in Italy, the grape is much used for making sweet sparkling wines, as in Asti Spumante or Moscato d'Asti. There are several appellations in south-west France for inexpensive Muscats made rather like port, part-fermented before the addition of grape alcohol to halt the conversion of sugar into alcohol, creating a sweet and heady *vin doux naturel*. Dry Muscat wines, when well made, have a delicious sweet aroma but a refreshing, light touch with flavours reminiscent variously of orange blossom, wood smoke and grapefruit.

must – New-pressed grape juice prior to fermentation.

N

Navarra – DO wine-producing region of northern Spain adjacent to, and overshadowed by, Rioja. Navarra's wines can be startlingly akin to their neighbouring rivals, and sometimes rather better value for money.

négociant – In France, a dealer-producer who buys wines from growers and matures and/or blends them for sale under his or her own label. Purists can be a bit sniffy about these entrepreneurs, claiming that only the vine-grower with his or her own winemaking set-up can make truly authentic stuff, but the truth is that many of the best wines of France are *négociant*-produced – especially at the humbler end of the price scale. *Négociants* are often identified on wine labels as *négociant-éleveur* (literally 'dealer-bringer-up'), meaning that the wine has been matured, blended and bottled by the party in question.

Negroamaro – Black grape variety mainly of Puglia, the much-lauded wine region of south-east Italy. Dense, earthy red wines with ageing potential and plenty of alcohol. The grape behind Copertino, Salice Salentio and Squinzano.

Nerello Mascalese – Black grape of Sicily making light, flavoursome and alcoholic reds.

Nero d'Avola – Black grape variety of Sicily and southern Italy. It makes deep-coloured wines that, given half a chance, can develop intensity and richness with age.

non-vintage – A wine is described as such when it has been blended from the harvests of more than one year. A non-vintage wine is not necessarily an inferior one, but under quality-control regulations around the world, still table wines most usually derive solely from one year's grape crop to qualify for appellation status. Champagnes and sparkling wines are mostly blended from several vintages, as are fortified wines, such as basic port and sherry.

nose – In the vocabulary of the wine-taster, the nose is the scent of a wine. Sounds a bit dotty, but it makes a sensible enough alternative to the rather bald 'smell'. The use of the word 'perfume' implies that the wine smells particularly good. 'Aroma' is used specifically to describe a wine that smells as it should, as in 'this burgundy has the authentic strawberry-raspberry aroma of Pinot Noir'.

O

oak – Most of the world's costliest wines are matured in new or nearly new oak barrels, giving additional opulence of flavour. Of late, many cheaper wines have been getting the oak treatment, too, in older, cheaper casks, or simply by having sacks of oak chippings poured into their steel or fibreglass holding tanks. 'Oak aged' on a label is likely to indicate the latter treatments. But the overtly oaked wines of Australia have in some cases been so overdone that there is now a reactive trend whereby some producers proclaim their wines – particularly Chardonnays – as 'unoaked' on the label, thereby asserting that the flavours are more naturally achieved.

Oltrepo Pavese – Wine-producing zone of Piedmont, north-west Italy. The name means 'south of Pavia across the [river] Po' and the wines, both white and red, can be excellent quality and value for money.

organic wine – As in other sectors of the food industry, demand for organically made wine is – or appears to be – growing. As a rule, a wine qualifies as organic if it comes entirely from grapes grown in vineyards cultivated without the use of synthetic materials, and made in a winery where chemical treatments or additives are shunned with similar vigour. In fact, there are plenty of winemakers in the world using organic methods, but who disdain to label their bottles as such. Wines proclaiming their organic status used to carry the same sort of premium as their counterparts round the corner in the fruit, vegetable and meat aisles. But organic viticulture is now commonplace and there seems little price impact. There is no single worldwide (or even Europe-wide) standard for organic food or wine, so you pretty much have to take the producer's word for it.

P

Pasqua – One of the biggest and, it should be said, best wine producers of the Veneto region of north-west Italy.

Passetoutgrains – Bourgogne Passetoutgrains is a generic appellation of the Burgundy region, France. The word loosely means 'any grapes allowed' and is supposed specifically to designate a red wine made with Gamay grapes as well as Burgundy's principal black variety, Pinot Noir, in a ratio of two parts Gamay to one of Pinot. The wine is usually relatively inexpensive, and relatively uninteresting, too.

Pays d'Oc – Shortened form under recent rule changes of French wine designation Vin de Pays d'Oc. All other similar regional designations can be similarly abbreviated.

Pecorino – White grape variety of mid-eastern Italy currently in vogue for well-coloured dry white varietal wines.

Periquita – Black grape variety of southern Portugal. Makes rather exotic spicy reds. Name means 'parrot'.

Perricone – Black grape variety of Sicily. Low-acid red wines.

PET – It's what they call plastic wine bottles – lighter to transport and allegedly as ecological as glass. Polyethylene terephthalate.

Petit Verdot – Black grape variety of Bordeaux used to give additional colour, density and spiciness to Cabernet Sauvignon-dominated blends. Mostly a minority player at home, but in Australia and California it is grown as the principal variety for some big hearty reds of real character.

petrol – When white wines from certain grapes, especially Riesling, are allowed to age in the bottle for longer than a year or two, they can take on a spirity aroma reminiscent of petrol or diesel. In grand mature German wines, this is considered a very good thing.

Picpoul – Grape variety of southern France. Best known in Picpoul de Pinet, a dry white from near Carcassonne in the Languedoc, newly elevated to AOP status. The name Picpoul (also Piquepoul) means 'stings the lips' – referring to the natural high acidity of the juice.

Piemonte – North-western province of Italy, which we call Piedmont, known for the spumante wines of the town of Asti, plus expensive Barbaresco and Barolo and better-value varietal red wines from Barbera and Dolcetto grapes.

Pinotage – South Africa's own black grape variety. Makes red wines ranging from light and juicy to dark, strong and long-lived. It's a cross between Pinot Noir and a grape the South Africans used to call Hermitage (thus the portmanteau name) but turns out to have been Cinsault.

Pinot Blanc – White grape variety principally of Alsace, France. Florally perfumed, exotically fruity dry white wines.

Pinot Grigio – White grape variety of northern Italy. Wines bearing its name are perplexingly fashionable. Good examples have an interesting smoky-pungent aroma and keen, slaking fruit. But most are dull. Originally French, it is at its best in the lushly exotic Pinot Gris wines of Alsace and is also successfully cultivated in Germany and New Zealand.

Pinot Noir – The great black grape of Burgundy, France. It makes all the region's fabulously expensive red wines. Notoriously difficult to grow in warmer climates, it is nevertheless cultivated by countless intrepid winemakers in the New World intent on reproducing the magic appeal of red burgundy. California and New Zealand have come closest, but rarely at prices much below those for the real thing. Some Chilean Pinot Noirs are inexpensive and worth trying.

Pouilly Fuissé – Village and AC of the Mâconnais region of southern Burgundy in France. Dry white wines from Chardonnay grapes. Wines are among the highest rated of the Mâconnais.

Pouilly Fumé – Village and AC of the Loire Valley in France. Dry white wines from Sauvignon Blanc grapes. Similar 'pebbly', 'grassy' or even 'gooseberry' style to neighbouring AC Sancerre. The notion put about by some enthusiasts that Pouilly Fumé is 'smoky' is surely nothing more than word association with the name.

Primitivo – Black grape variety of southern Italy, especially the region of Puglia. Named from Latin *primus* for first, the grape is among the earliest-ripening of all varieties. The wines are typically dense and dark in colour with plenty of alcohol, and have an earthy, spicy style. Often a real bargain.

Priorat – Emerging wine region of Catalonia, Spain. Highly valued red wines from Garnacha and other varieties.

Prosecco – White grape variety of Italy's Veneto region known entirely for the softly sparkling wine it makes. The best come from the DOCG Conegliano-Valdobbiadene, made as spumante ('foaming') wines in pressurised tanks, typically to 11 per cent alcohol and ranging from softly sweet to crisply dry. Now trendy, but the cheap wines – one leading brand comes in a can – are of very variable quality.

Puglia – The region occupying the 'heel' of southern Italy, lately making many good, inexpensive wines from indigenous grape varieties.

Q

QbA – German, standing for Qualitätswein bestimmter Anbaugebiete. It means 'quality wine from designated areas' and implies that the wine is made from grapes with a minimum level of ripeness, but it's by no means a guarantee of exciting quality. Only wines labelled QmP (see next entry) can be depended upon to be special.

QmP – Stands for Qualitätswein mit Prädikat. These are the serious wines of Germany, made without the addition of sugar to 'improve' them. To qualify for QmP status, the grapes must reach a level of ripeness as measured on a sweetness scale – all according to Germany's fiendishly complicated wine-quality regulations. Wines from grapes that reach the stated minimum level of sweetness qualify for the description of Kabinett. The next level up earns the rank of Spätlese, meaning 'late-picked'. Kabinett wines can be expected to be dry and brisk in style, and Spätlese wines a little bit riper and fuller. The next grade up, Auslese, meaning 'selected harvest', indicates a wine made from super-ripe grapes; it will be golden in colour and honeyed in flavour. A generation ago, these wines were as valued, and as expensive, as any of the world's grandest appellations.

Quincy – AC of Loire Valley, France, known for pebbly-dry white wines from Sauvignon grapes. The wines are forever compared to those of nearby and much better-known Sancerre – and Quincy often represents better value for money. Pronounced 'KAN-see'.

Quinta – Portuguese for farm or estate. It precedes the names of many of Portugal's best-known wines. It is pronounced 'KEEN-ta'.

R

racy – Evocative wine-tasting description for wine that thrills the tastebuds with a rush of exciting sensations. Good Rieslings often qualify.

raisiny – Wines from grapes that have been very ripe or overripe at harvest can take on a smell and flavour akin to the concentrated, heat-dried sweetness of raisins. As a minor element in the character of a wine, this can add to the appeal but as a dominant characteristic it is a fault.

rancio – Spanish term harking back to Roman times when wines were commonly stored in jars outside, exposed to the sun, so they oxidised and took on a burnt sort of flavour. Today, *rancio* describes a baked – and by no means unpleasant – flavour in fortified wines, particularly sherry and Madeira.

Reserva – In Portugal and Spain, this has genuine significance. The Portuguese use it for special wines with a higher alcohol level and longer ageing, although the precise periods vary between regions. In Spain, especially in the Navarra and Rioja regions, it means the wine must have had at least a year in oak and two in bottle before release.

reserve – On French (as *réserve*) or other wines, this implies special-quality, longer-aged wines, but has no official significance.

Retsina – The universal white wine of Greece. It has been traditionally made in Attica, the region of Athens, for a very long time, and is said to owe its origins and name to the ancient custom of sealing amphorae (terracotta jars) of the wine with a gum made from pine resin. Some of the flavour of the resin inevitably transmitted itself into the wine, and ancient Greeks acquired a lasting taste for it.

Reuilly – AC of Loire Valley, France, for crisp dry whites from Sauvignon grapes. Pronounced 'RER-yee'.

Ribatejo – Emerging wine region of Portugal. Worth seeking out on labels of red wines in particular, because new winemakers are producing lively stuff from distinctive indigenous grapes such as Castelao and Trincadeira.

Ribera del Duero – Classic wine region of north-west Spain lying along the River Duero (which crosses the border to become Portugal's Douro, forming the valley where port comes from). It is home to an estate rather oddly named Vega Sicilia, where red wines of epic quality are made and sold at equally epic prices. Further down the scale, some very good reds are made, too.

Riesling – The noble grape variety of Germany. It is correctly pronounced 'REEZ-ling', not 'RICE-ling'. Once notorious as the grape behind all those boring 'medium' Liebfraumilches and Niersteiners, this grape has had a bad press. In fact, there has never been much, if any, Riesling in Germany's cheap-and-nasty plonks. But the country's best wines, the so-called Qualitätswein mit Prädikat grades, are made almost exclusively with Riesling. These wines range from crisply fresh and appley styles to extravagantly fruity, honeyed wines from late-harvested grapes. Excellent Riesling wines are also made in Alsace and now in Australia.

Rioja – The principal fine-wine region of Spain, in the country's north east. The pricier wines are noted for their vanilla-pod richness from long ageing in oak casks. Tempranillo and Garnacha grapes make the reds, Viura the whites.

Ripasso – A particular style of Valpolicella wine. New wine is partially refermented in vats that have been used to make the Recioto reds (wines made from semi-dried grapes), thus creating a bigger, smoother version of usually light and pale Valpolicella.

Riserva – In Italy, a wine made only in the best vintages, and allowed longer ageing in cask and bottle.

Rivaner – Alternative name for Germany's Müller-Thurgau grape, the life-blood of Liebfraumilch.

Riverland – Vineyard region to the immediate north of the Barossa Valley of South Australia, extending east into New South Wales.

Roditis – White grape variety of Greece, known for fresh dry whites with decent acidity, often included in retsina.

rosso – Red wine, Italy.

Rosso Conero – DOC red wine made in the environs of Ancona in the Marches, Italy. Made from the Montepulciano grape, the wine can provide excellent value for money.

Ruby Cabernet – Black grape variety of California, created by crossing Cabernet Sauvignon and Carignan. Makes soft and squelchy red wine at home and in South Africa.

Rueda – DO of north-west Spain making first-class refreshing dry whites from the indigenous Verdejo grape, imported Sauvignon, and others. Exciting quality, and prices are keen.

Rully – AC of Chalonnais region of southern Burgundy, France. White wines from Chardonnay and red wines from Pinot Noir grapes. Both can be very good and are substantially cheaper than their more northerly Burgundian neighbours. Pronounced 'ROO-yee'.

S

Saint Emilion – AC of Bordeaux, France. Centred on the romantic hill town of St Emilion, this famous sub-region makes some of the grandest red wines of France, but also some of the best-value ones. Less fashionable than the Médoc region on the opposite (west) bank of the River Gironde that bisects Bordeaux, St Emilion wines are made largely with the Merlot grape, and are relatively quick to mature. The top wines are classified *1er grand cru classé* and are madly expensive, but many more are classified respectively *grand cru classé* and *grand cru*, and these designations can be seen as a fairly trustworthy indicator of quality. There are several 'satellite' St Emilion ACs named after the villages at their centres, notably Lussac St Emilion, Montagne St Emilion and Puisseguin St Emilion. Some excellent wines are made by estates within these ACs, and at relatively affordable prices thanks to the comparatively humble status of their satellite designations.

Salento – Up-and-coming wine region of southern Italy. Many good bargain reds from local grapes including Nero d'Avola and Primitivo.

Sancerre – AC of the Loire Valley, France, renowned for flinty-fresh Sauvignon whites and rarer Pinot Noir reds. These wines are never cheap, and recent tastings make it plain that only the best-made, individual-producer wines are worth the money. Budget brands seem mostly dull.

Sangiovese – The local black grape of Tuscany, Italy. It is the principal variety used for Chianti and is now widely planted in Latin America – often making delicious, Chianti-like wines with characteristic cherryish-but-deeply-ripe fruit and a dry, clean finish. Chianti wines have become (unjustifiably) expensive in recent years and cheaper Italian wines such as those called Sangiovese di Toscana make a consoling substitute.

Saumur – Town and appellation of Loire Valley, France. Characterful minerally red wines from Cabernet Franc grapes, and some whites. The once-popular sparkling wines from Chenin Blanc grapes are now little seen in Britain.

Saumur-Champigny – Separate appellation for red wines from Cabernet Franc grapes of Saumur in the Loire, sometimes very good and lively.

Sauvignon Blanc – French white grape variety now grown worldwide. New Zealand is successfully challenging the long supremacy of French ACs such as Sancerre. The wines are characterised by aromas of gooseberry, fresh-cut grass, even asparagus. Flavours are often described as 'grassy' or 'nettly'.

sec – Dry wine style. French.

secco – Dry wine style. Italian.

Semillon – White grape variety originally of Bordeaux, where it is blended with Sauvignon Blanc to make fresh dry whites and, when harvested very late in the season, the ambrosial sweet whites of Barsac, Sauternes and other appellations. Even in the driest wines, the grape can be recognised from its honeyed, sweet-pineapple, even banana-like aromas. Now widely planted in Australia and Latin America, and frequently blended with Chardonnay to make dry whites, some of them interesting.

sherry – The great aperitif wine of Spain, centred on the Andalusian city of Jerez (from which the name 'sherry' is an English mispronunciation). There is a lot of sherry-style wine in the world, but only the authentic wine from Jerez and the neighbouring producing towns of Puerta de Santa Maria and Sanlucar de Barrameda may label their wines as such. The Spanish drink real sherry – very dry and fresh, pale in colour and served well-chilled – called fino and manzanilla, and darker but naturally dry variations called amontillado, palo cortado and oloroso.

Shiraz – Australian name for the Syrah grape. The variety is the most widely planted of any in Australia, and makes red wines of wildly varying quality, characterised by dense colour, high alcohol, spicy fruit and generous, cushiony texture.

Somontano – Wine region of north-east Spain. Name means 'under the mountains' – in this case the Pyrenees – and the region has had DO status since 1984. Much innovative winemaking here, with New World styles emerging. Some very good buys. A region to watch.

souple – French wine-tasting term that translates into English as 'supple' or even 'docile' as in 'pliable', but I understand it in the vinous context to mean muscular but soft – a wine with tannin as well as soft fruit.

Spätlese – *See* QmP.

spirity – Some wines, mostly from the New World, are made from grapes so ripe at harvest that their high alcohol content can be detected through a mildly burning sensation on the tongue, similar to the effect of sipping a spirit.

spritzy – Describes a wine with a barely detectable sparkle. Some young wines are intended to have this elusive fizziness; in others it is a fault.

spumante – Sparkling wine of Italy. Asti Spumante is the best known, from the town of Asti in the north-west Italian province of Piemonte. The term describes wines that are fully sparkling. Frizzante wines have a less vigorous mousse.

stalky – A useful tasting term to describe red wines with flavours that make you think the stalks from the grape bunches must have been fermented along with the must (juice). Young Bordeaux reds very often have this mild astringency. In moderation it's fine, but if it dominates it probably signifies the wine is at best immature and at worst badly made.

Stellenbosch – Town and region at the heart of South Africa's burgeoning wine industry. It's an hour's drive from Cape Town and the source of much of the country's cheaper wine. Quality is variable, and the name Stellenbosch on a label can't (yet, anyway) be taken as a guarantee of quality.

stony – Wine-tasting term for keenly dry white wines. It's meant to indicate a wine of purity and real quality, with just the right match of fruit and acidity.

structured – Good wines are not one-dimensional, they have layers of flavour and texture. A structured wine has phases of enjoyment: the 'attack', or first impression in the mouth; the middle palate as the wine is held in the mouth; and the lingering aftertaste.

summer fruit – Wine-tasting term intended to convey a smell or taste of soft fruits such as strawberries and raspberries – without having to commit too specifically to which.

superiore – On labels of Italian wines, this is more than an idle boast. Under DOC rules, wines must qualify for the *superiore* designation by reaching one or more specified quality levels, usually a higher alcohol content or an additional period of maturation. Frascati, for example, qualifies for DOC status at 11.5 per cent alcohol, but to be classified *superiore* must have 12 per cent alcohol.

sur lie – Literally, 'on the lees'. It's a term now widely used on the labels of Muscadet wines, signifying that after fermentation has died down, the new wine has been left in the tank over the winter on the lees – the detritus of yeasts and other interesting compounds left over from the turbid fermentation process. The idea is that additional interest is imparted into the flavour of the wine.

Syrah – The noble grape of the Rhône Valley, France. Makes very dark, dense wine characterised by peppery, tarry aromas. Now planted all over southern France and farther afield. In Australia, where it makes wines ranging from disagreeably jam-like plonks to wonderfully rich and silky keeping wines, it is known as Shiraz.

T

table wine – Wine that is unfortified and of an alcoholic strength, for UK tax purposes anyway, of no more than 15 per cent. I use the term to distinguish, for example, between the red table wines of the Douro Valley in Portugal and the region's better-known fortified wine, port.

Tafelwein – Table wine, German. The humblest quality designation, which doesn't usually bode very well.

tank method – Bulk-production process for sparkling wines. Base wine undergoes secondary fermentation in a large, sealed vat rather than in individual closed bottles. Also known as the Charmat method after the name of the inventor of the process.

Tai – White grape variety of north-east Italy, a relative of Sauvignon Blanc. Also known in Italy as Tocai Friulano or, more correctly, Friulano.

Tannat – Black grape of south-west France, notably for wines of Madiran, and lately named as the variety most beneficial to health thanks to its outstanding antioxidant content.

tannin – Well known as the film-forming, teeth-coating component in tea, tannin is a natural compound that occurs in black grape skins and acts as a natural preservative in wine. Its noticeable presence in wine is regarded as a good thing. It gives young everyday reds their dryness, firmness of flavour and backbone. And it helps high-quality reds to retain their lively fruitiness for many years. A grand Bordeaux red when first made, for example, will have purply-sweet, rich fruit and mouth-puckering tannin, but after ten years or so this will have evolved into a delectably fruity, mature wine in which the formerly parching effects of the tannin have receded almost completely, leaving the shade of 'residual tannin' that marks out a great wine approaching maturity.

Tarrango – Black grape variety of Australia.

tarry – On the whole, winemakers don't like critics to say their wines evoke the redolence of road repairs, but I can't help using this term to describe the agreeable, sweet, 'burnt' flavour that is often found at the centre of the fruit in wines from Argentina, Italy and Portugal in particular.

TCA – Dreaded ailment in wine, usually blamed on faulty corks. It stands for 246 *trichloroanisol* and is characterised by a horrible musty smell and flavour in the affected wine. It is largely because of the current plague of TCA that so many wine producers worldwide are now going over to polymer 'corks' and screwcaps.

tears – The colourless alcohol in the wine left clinging to the inside of the glass after the contents have been swirled. Persistent tears (also known as 'legs') indicate a wine of good concentration.

Tempranillo – The great black grape of Spain. Along with Garnacha (Grenache in France) it makes all red Rioja and Navarra wines and, under many pseudonyms, is an important or exclusive contributor to the wines of many other regions of Spain. It is also widely cultivated in South America.

Teroldego – Black grape variety of Trentino, northern Italy. Often known as Teroldego Rotaliano after the Rotaliano region where most of the vineyards lie. Deep-coloured, assertive, green-edged red wines.

tinto – On Spanish labels indicates a deeply coloured red wine. Clarete denotes a paler colour. Also Portuguese.

Toro – Quality wine region east of Zamora, Spain.

Torrontes – White grape variety of Argentina. Makes soft, dry wines often with delicious grapey-spicy aroma, similar in style to the classic dry Muscat wines of Alsace, but at more accessible prices.

Touraine – Region encompassing a swathe of the Loire Valley, France. Non-AC wines may be labelled 'Sauvignon de Touraine' etc.

Touriga Nacional – The most valued black grape variety of the Douro Valley in Portugal, where port is made. The name Touriga now appears on an increasing number of table wines made as sidelines by the port producers. They can be very good, with the same spirity aroma and sleek flavours of port itself, minus the fortification.

Traminer – Grape variety, the same as Gewürztraminer.

Trebbiano – The workhorse white grape of Italy. A productive variety that is easy to cultivate, it seems to be included in just about every ordinary white wine of the entire nation – including Frascati, Orvieto and Soave. It is the same grape as France's Ugni Blanc. There are, however, distinct regional variations of the grape. Trebbiano di Lugana makes a distinctive white in the DOC of the name, sometimes very good, while Trebbiano di

Toscana makes a major contribution to the distinctly less interesting dry whites of Chianti country.

Trincadeira Preta – Portuguese black grape variety native to the port-producing vineyards of the Douro Valley (where it goes under the name Tinta Amarella). In southern Portugal, it produces dark and sturdy table wines.

trocken – 'Dry' German wine. It's a recent trend among commercial-scale producers in the Rhine and Mosel to label their wines with this description in the hope of reassuring consumers that the contents do not resemble the dreaded sugar-water Liebfraumilch-type plonks of the bad old days. But the description does have a particular meaning under German wine law, namely that there is only a low level of unfermented sugar lingering in the wine (9 grams per litre, if you need to know), and this can leave the wine tasting rather austere.

U

Ugni Blanc – The most widely cultivated white grape variety of France and the mainstay of many a cheap dry white wine. To date it has been better known as the provider of base wine for distilling into armagnac and cognac, but lately the name has been appearing on wine labels. Technology seems to be improving the performance of the grape. The curious name is pronounced 'OON-yee', and is the same variety as Italy's ubiquitous Trebbiano.

Utiel-Requena – Region and *Denominación de Origen* of Mediterranean Spain inland from Valencia. Principally red wines from Bobal, Garnacha and Tempranillo grapes grown at relatively high altitude, between 600 and 900 metres.

V

Vacqueyras – Village of the southern Rhône Valley of France in the region better known for its generic appellation, the Côtes du Rhône. Vacqueyras can date its winemaking history all the way back to 1414, but has only been producing under its own village AC since 1991. The wines, from Grenache and Syrah grapes, can be wonderfully silky and intense, spicy and long-lived.

Valdepeñas – An island of quality production amidst the ocean of mediocrity that is Spain's La Mancha region – where most of the grapes are grown for distilling into the head-banging brandies of Jerez. Valdepeñas reds are made from a grape they call the Cencibel – which turns out to be a very close relation of the Tempranillo grape that is the mainstay of the fine but expensive red wines of Rioja. Again, like Rioja, Valdepeñas wines are matured in oak casks to give them a vanilla-rich smoothness. Among bargain reds, Valdepeñas is a name to look out for.

Valpolicella – Red wine of Verona, Italy. Good examples have ripe, cherry fruit and a pleasingly dry finish. Unfortunately, there are many bad examples of Valpolicella. Shop with circumspection. Valpolicella Classico wines, from the best vineyards clustered around the town, are more reliable. Those additionally labelled *superiore* have higher alcohol and some bottle age.

vanilla – Ageing wines in oak barrels (or, less picturesquely, adding oak chips to wine in huge concrete vats) imparts a range of characteristics including a smell of vanilla from the ethyl vanilline naturally given off by oak.

varietal – A varietal wine is one named after the grape variety (one or more) from which it is made. Nearly all everyday wines worldwide are now labelled in this way. It is salutary to contemplate that until the present wine boom began in the 1980s, wines described thus were virtually unknown outside Germany and one or two quirky regions of France and Italy.

vegan-friendly – My informal way of noting that a wine is claimed to have been made not only with animal-product-free finings (*see* vegetarian wine) but without any animal-related products whatsoever, such as manure in the vineyards.

vegetal – A tasting note definitely open to interpretation. It suggests a smell or flavour reminiscent less of fruit (apple, pineapple, strawberry and the like) than of something leafy or even root based. Some wines are evocative (to some tastes) of beetroot, cabbage or even unlikelier vegetable flavours – and these characteristics may add materially to the attraction of the wine.

vegetarian wine – Wines labelled 'suitable for vegetarians' have been made without the assistance of animal products for 'fining' – clarifying – before bottling. Gelatine, egg whites, isinglass from fish bladders and casein from milk are among the items shunned, usually in favour of bentonite, an absorbent clay first found at Benton in the US state of Montana.

Verdejo – White grape of the Rueda region in north-west Spain. It can make superbly perfumed crisp dry whites of truly distinctive character and has helped make Rueda one of the best white-wine sources of Europe. No relation to Verdelho.

Verdelho – Portuguese grape variety once mainly used for a medium-dry style of Madeira, also called Verdelho, but now rare. The vine is now prospering in Australia, where it can make well-balanced dry whites with fleeting richness and lemon-lime acidity.

Verdicchio – White grape variety of Italy best known in the DOC zone of Castelli di Jesi in the Adriatic wine region of the Marches. Dry white wines once known for little more than their naff amphora-style bottles but now gaining a reputation for interesting, herbaceous flavours of recognisable character.

Vermentino – White grape variety principally of Italy, especially Sardinia. Makes florally scented soft dry whites.

Vieilles vignes – Old vines. Many French producers like to claim on their labels that the wine within is from vines of notable antiquity. While it's true that vines don't produce useful grapes for the first few years after planting, it is uncertain whether vines of much greater age – say 25 years plus – than others actually make better fruit. There are no regulations governing the use of the term, so it's not a reliable indicator anyway.

Vin de France – In effect, the new Vin de Table of France's morphing wine laws. The term Vin de Table has just about disappeared – or should have, under new legislation introduced in 2010 – and Vin de France installed as the designation of a wine guaranteed to have been produced in France. The label may state the vintage (if all the wine in the blend does come from a single year's harvest) and the grape varieties that constitute the wine. It may not state the region of France from which the wine comes.

vin de liqueur – Sweet style of white wine mostly from the Pyrenean region of south-westernmost France, made by adding a little spirit to the new wine before it has fermented out, halting the fermentation and retaining sugar.

vin de pays – 'Country wine' of France. The French map is divided up into more than 100 vin de pays regions. Introduced in 1968 and regularly revised ever since, it's the wine-quality designation between basic Vin de France and AOC/AOP. Although being superseded by the more recently introduced IGP (*qv*), there are more than 150 producing areas permitted to use the description vin de pays. Some vin de pays areas are huge: the Vin de Pays d'Oc (named after the Languedoc region) covers much of the Midi and Provence. Plenty of wines bearing this humble designation are of astoundingly high quality and certainly compete with New World counterparts for interest and value. *See* Indication Géographique Protégée.

vin de table – Formerly official designation of generic French wine, now used only informally. *See* Vin de France.

vin doux naturel – Sweet, mildly fortified wine of southern France. A little spirit is added during the winemaking process, halting the fermentation by killing the yeast before it has consumed all the sugars – hence the pronounced sweetness of the wine.

vin gris – Rosé wine from Provence.

Vinho de mesa – 'Table wine' of Portugal.

Vino da tavola – The humblest official classification of Italian wine. Much ordinary plonk bears this designation, but the bizarre quirks of Italy's wine laws dictate that some of that country's finest wines are also classed as mere vino da tavola (table wine). If an expensive Italian wine is labelled as such, it doesn't mean it will be a disappointment.

Vino de mesa – 'Table wine' of Spain. Usually very ordinary.

vintage – The grape harvest. The year displayed on bottle labels is the year of the harvest. Wines bearing no date have been blended from the harvests of two or more years.

Viognier – A grape variety once exclusive to the northern Rhône Valley in France where it makes a very chi-chi wine, Condrieu, usually costing £20 plus. Now, the Viognier is grown more widely, in North and South America as well as elsewhere in France, and occasionally produces soft, marrowy whites that echo the grand style of Condrieu itself. The Viognier is now commonly blended with Shiraz in red winemaking in Australia and South Africa. It does not dilute the colour and is confidently believed by highly experienced winemakers to enhance the quality. Steve Webber, in charge of winemaking at the revered De Bortoli estates in the Yarra Valley region of Victoria, Australia, puts between two and five per cent Viognier in with some of his Shiraz wines. 'I think it's the perfume,' he told me. 'It gives some femininity to the wine.'

Viura – White grape variety of Rioja, Spain. Also widely grown elsewhere in Spain under the name Macabeo. Wines have a blossomy aroma and are dry, but sometimes soft at the expense of acidity.

Vouvray – AC of the Loire Valley, France, known for still and sparkling dry white wines and sweet, still whites from late-harvested grapes. The wines, all from Chenin Blanc grapes, have a unique capacity for unctuous softness combined with lively freshness – an effect best portrayed in the demi-sec (slightly sweet) wines, which can be delicious and keenly priced. Unfashionable, but worth looking out for.

Vranac – Black grape variety of the Balkans known for dense colour and tangy-bitter edge to the flavour. Best enjoyed in situ.

W

weight – In an ideal world the weight of a wine is determined by the ripeness of the grapes from which it has been made. In some cases the weight is determined merely by the quantity of sugar added during the production process. A good, genuine wine described as having weight is one in which there is plenty of alcohol and 'extract' – colour and flavour from the grapes. Wine enthusiasts judge weight by swirling the wine in the glass and then examining the 'legs' or 'tears' left clinging to the inside of the glass after the contents have subsided. Alcohol gives these runlets a dense, glycerine-like condition, and if they cling for a long time, the wine is deemed to have weight – a very good thing in all honestly made wines.

Winzergenossenschaft – One of the many very lengthy and peculiar words regularly found on labels of German wines. This means a winemaking co-operative. Many excellent German wines are made by these associations of growers.

woodsap – A subjective tasting note. Some wines have a fleeting bitterness, which is not a fault, but an interesting balancing factor amidst very ripe flavours. The effect somehow evokes woodsap.

X

Xarel-lo – One of the main grape varieties for cava, the sparkling wine of Spain.

Xinomavro – Black grape variety of Greece. It retains its acidity even in the very hot conditions that prevail in many Greek vineyards, where harvests tend to over-ripen and make cooked-tasting wines. Modern winemaking techniques are capable of making well-balanced wines from Xinomavro.

Y

Yecla – Town and DO wine region of eastern Spain, close to Alicante, making lots of interesting, strong-flavoured red and white wines, often at bargain prices.

yellow – White wines are not white at all, but various shades of yellow – or, more poetically, gold. Some white wines with opulent richness even have a flavour I cannot resist calling yellow – reminiscent of butter.

Z

Zibibbo – Sicilian white grape variety synonymous with north African variety Muscat of Alexandria. Scantily employed in sweet winemaking, and occasionally for drier styles.

Zinfandel – Black grape variety of California. Makes brambly reds, some of which can age very gracefully, and 'blush' whites – actually pink, because a little of the skin colour is allowed to leach into the must. The vine is also planted in Australia and South America. The Primitivo of southern Italy is said to be a related variety, but makes a very different kind of wine.

Index